REINHOLD PLASTICS
APPLICATIONS SERIES

VINYL RESINS

by

W. MAYO SMITH

Director, Research and Development
Escambia Chemical Corporation
Research Center
Wilton, Connecticut

REINHOLD PUBLISHING CORPORATION
NEW YORK
CHAPMAN & HALL, LTD., LONDON

Copyright 1958 by
REINHOLD PUBLISHING CORPORATION

Library of Congress Catalog Card Number: 58-12825

Printed in the U.S.A.

Reinhold Plastics Applications Series

Many factors are involved in the determination of the optimum application of a plastic, and the correct application in a very real sense determines the true worth of a material. The best plastic to use for a given product must not only fill the required physical specifications, but it also must be competitively priced and often offer esthetic satisfaction.

Realizing the importance of correct application in the whole gamut of plastics activity, the Reinhold Publishing Corporation, late in 1956, decided to publish a series of short books emphasizing the applications of the various plastics materials and of their fabrication processes—each book to cover one type of material or one process. The present volume by W. Mayo Smith is the seventh of this series. Those already published are the volumes on polyethylene, polyurethanes, polyamide resins, plastic sheet forming, cellulosics, and fluorocarbons. Eight additional volumes are now in preparation; thus this is the mid-point in the series as at present projected.

The series is semi-technical—that is, one does not need to be a chemist to understand the various volumes. The authors have kept in mind as probable readers such industrial men and women as: design engineers, equipment manufacturers, producers of packages, manufacturers of packaging machinery, students at technical schools and, of course, all people in the plastics industry—material manufacturers, molders, extruders, fabricators.

In addition to the above, it is hoped that each title will appeal to readers in specialized categories. Plastics from which fibers are made may be of interest to tire and fabric manufacturers. A book such as this one on vinyls, which materials are favorable for production of sheets, may have value for manufacturers of handbags and luggage. Similarly, other titles may appeal to manufacturers of paints, recorder tapes, upholstery, plywood and furniture.

With this program at its mid-point, it is with enthusiasm that this seventh book of the series is presented.

HERBERT R. SIMONDS, *Editor*

Titles Published

Cellulosics, *Walter Paist*

Fluorocarbons, *Merritt A. Rudner*

Plastic Sheet Forming, *Robert L. Butzko*

Polyamide Resins, *Don E. Floyd*

Polyethylene, *Theodore O. J. Kresser*

Polyurethanes, *Bernard A. Dombrow*

Titles in Preparation

Acrylic Resins, *Nathaniel C. Ratner*

Amino Resins, *John F. Blais*

Epoxy Resins, *Irving Skeist*

Gum Plastics, *M. Stafford Thompson*

Laminated Plastics, *Dan Duffin and Charles Nerzig*

Phenolic Resins, *D. F. Gould*

Polyesters, *John Lawrence*

Polystyrene, *Harold M. Hartong*

PREFACE

The vinyls constitute the most versatile and the largest selling family of plastics, and although considerable descriptive literature exists it is thought that there is a need for a relatively short book emphasizing their applications. To fill that need is what this book attempts.

Because of the many distinct types of vinyls, each of which is described with its typical applications, some duplication has been unavoidable and therefore the reader seeking knowledge of any specific application should refer to the index.

While the intent in this book has been to avoid highly technical material, some detailed descriptions have been necessarily involved. However it is hoped that a balance between technical and semi-technical coverage has been achieved so that the volume may appeal to a broad cross-section of readers.

The author wishes to express his appreciation to those companies which have supplied some of the information used in the preparation of this book. All manufacturers of the vinyl resins were solicited for information, as well as manufacturers of processing machinery and fabricators of vinyl products. Specific acknowledgment is made in the text whenever these contributions seemed to warrant it.

Particularly indebtedness to Miss Irene Petrone is offered for her valuable secretarial assistance in preparing the entire manuscript. The contribution of Mrs. Alice Alexander toward this same objective is also acknowledged.

W. Mayo Smith

Wilton, Conn.
June, 1958

CONTENTS

1. SCOPE OF THE VINYLS

Preliminary U. S. Tariff Commission figures for 1957 show that leading the plastics field was perhaps the most versatile of all plastics, the family of vinyl resins. Total vinyl types produced was 841.2 million lb, an increase of 11.8% over 1956. (Department of Commerce data estimate this production to be 860 million for 1957). PVC (polyvinyl chloride) and copolymer resins, 50% or more PVC, were 593 million. Styrene polymer was up 1.1% to 635.4 million, while cellulosics totaled 151 million, a gain of 3.5%. Polyester production increased 30.7% to 94.8 million, and polyethylene to 682.8, up 22.6%. Phenolic and other tar-acid resins dropped 7.1% to 475.9; urea and melamine resins were down 2.8% to 308.5 million lb.

Department of Commerce compilations for 1957 state alkyds produced totaled 430 million, the same as 1956; coumarone-indene and petroleum polymer resins 280 million, up 8%; rosin modification, about 130 million, down 2%; miscellaneous synthetic plastics and resins 220 million, up 14%.

Many widely varying opinions and statements concerning anticipated production of vinyl resins have been made. Some of these state that by 1960, and most assuredly by 1965, the production of all vinyl resins will exceed one billion pounds per year. The greatly expanding scope of vinyls in such presently relatively insignificant fields as agriculture, for example, may make one billion pound production by 1960 or 1965 entirely possible.

TABLE 1.1. VINYL CHLORIDE AND COPOLYMER CONSUMPTION OF RESIN PRODUCED IN U. S., 1952-1956 [a] (Millions of lb)

Use	1956 Lb	1955 Lb	1954 Lb	1953 Lb	1952 Lb
Film under 10 mils	78	83	69	66	79
Sheeting over 10 mils [b]	53	51	55	60	74
Fabric treatment	55	56	42	39	37
Paper treatment	8	8	7	6	7
Flooring	66	56	34	25	—
Molding and extrusion	205	183	148	115	105
Protective coating [c]	29	26	23	22	—
Miscellaneous [d]	74	58	34	26	37
Total	568	521	412	359	339

[a] Based on U. S. Tariff Commission reports for years 1952-1956.

[b] Prior to 1953, the sheeting figure included portions of such products as flooring and other items that are now reported in other classifications.

[c] Protective coatings were reported in miscellaneous in 1952.

[d] This is also an adjustment medium because of the complexities involved in separating vinyl resin uses into their various end use patterns; that is, the total over-all figure is fairly well established, but there is wide difference of opinion concerning the amount used for each end product.

NOTE: About 30 million lb of resin imported in 1955 and 1956 are not included in this breakdown. It is thought to have been used roughly as follows: 12 million lb for film, 10 million for sheeting, and 8 million for extrusion. Vinyl exports for 1957 are approximately 30 million lb of resin and 15 million lb of compound.

The homopolymer of vinyl chloride and its copolymers comprise the largest production and sale of resin in the vinyl family. As would be expected, marked discrepancies appear in various published data regarding these production figures and sale. In Tables 1.1 and 1.2 figures compiled by the U. S. Tariff Commission are given for the homopolymer of vinyl chloride and its copolymers produced in the United States in the years 1952 through 1957. It is observed that molding and extrusion of 215.9 million lb of resin is the largest single item in this breakdown in the year 1957. The next largest amount is production of film, this resulting in a 90.5 million lb usage. ("Film" is arbitrarily designed as the thickness of the material 10 mils or less, while "sheeting" is over 10 mils).

TABLE 1.2. VINYL AND VINYL COPOLYMER RESINS PRODUCTION
FOR 1957 [a]

	PVC and Copolymer Resins (50% or more vinyl chloride) million/lb resin content
Film	90.5
Sheeting	56.3
Molding and extrusion	216.0
Textile and paper treating and coating	66.4
Flooring	81.4
Protective coatings	31.5
All other uses	50.6
Total	592.7
All other vinyl resins for-	
Adhesives	41.3
All other uses	113.2
Total	154.5
Grand Total	747.2

[a] Source U. S. Tariff Commission Preliminary Report for 1957.

PVC sales for 1947 through 1957 and anticipated sales from 1958 through 1960 are presented in Table 1.3. Growth pattern of these sales is conservatively estimated in the years 1958 through 1960 at an anticipated growth rate of 8% overall per year. This indicates that by 1960, the sale of PVC and copolymer will be approximately 746,000,000 lb.

In Table 1.4, taken in part from *Modern Plastics,* consumption of calendered vinyl film is given. The growth picture here represents a total consumption of film in 1957 of 121,500,000 lb. Imported resin is excluded. This represents an increase of approximately 28,000,000 lb since 1953.

TABLE 1.3. VINYL CHLORIDE AND COPOLYMER SALES FOR 1947-1957; ANTICIPATED 1958-1960

Year	1947	1948	1949	1950	1951	1952	1953	1954	1955	1956	1957	Estimated at 8% Over-all Growth per Year		
												1958	1959	1960
Millions of lb	100	135	195	280	318	339	359	412	521	568	593	640	691	746

Includes resin used in the following categories:

1. Film
2. Sheeting
3. Calender coated fabrics
4. Dispersion for coated fabrics, slush molding, foam products, etc.
5. Flooring
6. Extrusion—shape and profile
7. Extrusion—wire and cable
8. Rigids for pipe and sheeting (extrusion and calender)

TABLE 1.4. PATTERN OF CONSUMPTION OF CALENDERED VINYL FILMS

Uses	1953 lb	1955 lb	1956 lb	1957 lb
Draperies, bedspreads, kitchen and bathroom curtains	23,000,000	15,000,000	14,000,000	14,000,000
Yard goods	10,000,000	9,000,000	8,000,000	6,000,000
Adhesive-backed film	—	1,000,000	4,500,000	6,000,000
Closet accessories	6,500,000	7,000,000	7,000,000	6,500,000
Shower curtains	6,000,000	7,000,000	8,500,000	8,800,000
Nursery goods	4,000,000	4,000,000	5,000,000	6,000,000
Baby pants and liners	2,400,000	3,000,000	3,300,000	3,500,000
Table covers	4,000,000	4,000,000	3,500,000	3,000,000
Appliance covers	3,000,000	2,500,000	2,500,000	3,000,000
Furniture covers, indoor and outdoor	3,000,000	3,500,000	3,500,000	2,500,000
Rainwear and outer-wear, including sportswear	10,000,000	12,000,000	9,500,000	9,000,000
Aprons, including industrial	1,500,000	3,000,000	3,000,000	2,500,000
Lamination and quilting for other than sportswear	—	8,000,000	11,000,000	15,500,000
Wall covering	—	4,000,000	6,000,000	6,500,000
Industrial tape	—	8,000,000	10,000,000	4,500,000
Inflatables	—	3,000,000	4,000,000	7,000,000
Industrial and miscellaneous	20,000,000	21,000,000	12,700,000	17,200,000
Total	93,400,000	115,000,000	116,000,000	121,500,000

An interesting picture is provided in Table 1.5 in which the PVC resin production capacities are given for all manufacturers. Bakelite and Goodrich are the largest manufacturers, having a combined production total of at least 425,000,000 lb. Planned expansions which have been announced and some which are speculated increase this 1957 capacity of 856,000,-000 to 975,000,000 lb.

6 *Vinyl Resins*

TABLE 1.5. PVC RESIN CAPACITIES
(000,000 #)

Company	Location	Capacity
1. Bakelite	S. Charleston, W. Va.; Texas City, Tex.	225-250
2. Diamond	Houston, Tex.	12- 25
3. Dow	Freeport, Tex.; Midland, Mich.	30- 35
4. Escambia Chemical	Pensacola, Fla.	50- 50
5. Firestone	Pottstown, Pa.	60- 60
6. General Tire	Ashtabula, Ohio	24- 36
7. Goodrich	Niagara Falls, N. Y.; Louisville, Ky.; Avon Lake, Ohio	200-225
8. Goodyear	Niagara Falls, N. Y.	35- 40
9. Monsanto	Indian Orchard, Mass.	100-125
10. Naugatuck	Painesville, Ohio	50- 50
Total		786-896 Present Capacity

Anticipated New Production 1957-8

Company	Capacity
11. Atlantic Tubing & Rubber Co. Cranston, R. I.	10- 10
12. Borden Chemical Peabody, Mass.	11- 12
13. Cary Chemical Flemington, N. J.	20- 20
14. Eleanora Chemical (Pantasote) Passaic, N. J.	6- 8
15. Great American Plastics Fitchburg, Mass.	4- 5
16. Insular Chemical (Ross & Roberts Rubber Corp. of America) Hicksville, N. Y.	5- 6
17. Presto Plastics Brooklyn, N. Y.	8- 10
18. Thompson Chemical (Apex Tire) Taunton, Mass.	6- 8
	70- 79
Total	786-896
Grand Total	856-975

The years 1956 and 1957 were marked by the entry of a number of other companies into the production field of polyvinyl chloride. With the exception of Escambia Chemical Corporation, these new producers are somewhat smaller than most of the established producers of PVC resin. Most of the new resin producers manufacture by suspension processes.

The strongly competitive PVC field requires intensive research, development and technical service which is supplied by most major manufacturers. A list of these establishments and their locations is given in Table 1.6.

TABLE 1.6. RESEARCH AND DEVELOPMENT TECHNICAL SERVICE LOCATIONS FOR PVC PRODUCERS

	Company	Research & Development	Technical Service
1.	Bakelite	Bloomfield, N. J.	Bound Brook, N. J.
2.	Escambia	Wilton, Conn.	Wilton, Conn.
3.	Diamond	Painesville, Ohio	Painesville, Ohio
4.	Dow	Midland, Mich.	Midland, Mich.
5.	Firestone	Akron, Ohio	Pottstown, Pa.
6.	General Tire	Akron, Ohio	Akron, Ohio
7.	Goodrich	Brecksville, Ohio	Avon Lake, Ohio
8.	Goodyear	Akron, Ohio	Akron, Ohio
9.	Monsanto	Springfield, Mass.	Springfield, Mass.
10.	Naugatuck	Naugatuck, Conn.	Naugatuck, Conn.

A further breakdown of consumption patterns of vinyl resins collected by the Stanford Research Institute is provided in Table 1.7. The marked discrepancy in the totals of Tables 1.7 and 1.1 is due mostly to variations in the miscellaneous use amounts and 73 million lb of polyvinyl acetate included in Table 1.7. This particular collection of a total of 703.3 million lb for 1955 and an estimated 752.4 million for 1956 and 804 million for 1957 is further represented by Figures 1.1 and 1.2. Figure 1.1 indicates that the 1955 production of polyvinyl chloride and its copolymers was 527,000,000 lb, polyvinyl acetate 73,000,000, while all other vinyls were 103,000,000

8   *Vinyl Resins*

lb. Figure 1.2 graphically represents the consumption pattern
of vinyl resins in the categories of molding and extrusion,
sheets and film, textile and paper treating and coating, adhesives and as protective coatings.

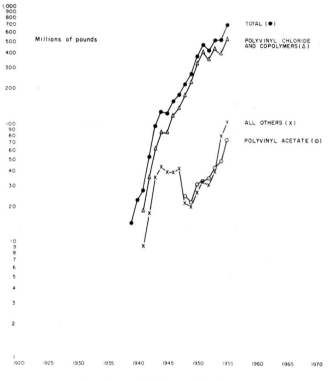

Figure 1.1. Production of vinyl resins.

Figures supplied by the Society of the Plastics Industry
estimate vinyl consumption in 1956 to have been 729.5
million lb, an increase of 10% over 1955. They similarly estimate polyethylene use for 1956 at 541 million, a 30% in-

crease over 1955. (See page 1 for 1957 figures). This of course suggests a close race for leadership in the years ahead. If the sales curves of the vinyls and of polyethylene are projected, they will meet in the year 1963.

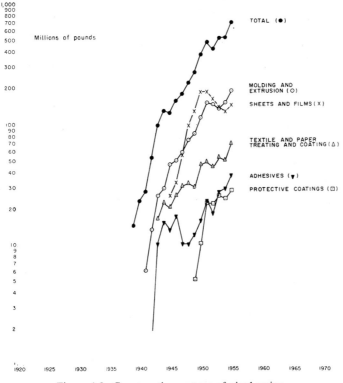

Figure 1.2. Consumption pattern of vinyl resins.

Whether the vinyls become the first one billion pound plastic remains to be seen. It is true that present day vinyl applications in some categories far outstrip well qualified predictions made only a few years ago. At a technical meeting in 1957, several capable observers stated privately that vinyl

Vinyl Resins

TABLE 1.7. CONSUMPTION PATTERN OF VINYL RESINS
(Millions of lb)

	Molding and Extrusion	Sheets and Films	Textile and Paper Treating and Coating	Flooring	Adhesives	Protective Coatings	Misc. Uses	Total
1939	—	—	—	—	—	—	14.2	14.2
1940	—	—	—	—	—	—	22.5	22.5
1941	6.0	—	—	—	—	—	21.0	27.0
1942	13.0	—	—	—	1.5	—	37.7	52.2
1943	25.0	—	16.0	—	10.0	—	44.5	95.6
1944	28.8	—	22.0	—	15.0	—	61.0	126.9
1945	45.8	25.0	20.0	—	13.0	—	18.9	122.7
1946	49.5	32.4	25.1	—	16.9	—	31.7	155.6
1947	57.8	54.6	30.1	—	10.0	—	25.0	177.4
1948	73.1	96.0	31.6	—	10.0	—	10.5	221.2
1949	82.2	126.5	29.5	—	11.9	5.0	12.6	267.7
1950	112.5	182.0	45.6	—	15.5	10.0	15.4	381.0
1951	149.1	183.0	47.5	—	22.8	22.1	51.2	475.8
1952	145.0	159.5	41.6	—	17.8	21.6	32.7	418.2
1953	133.0	137.2	51.4	24.3	26.9	24.8	118.1	515.9
1954	149.3	125.8	49.3	35.1	29.0	23.8	111.4	523.6
1955	193.8	141.6	67.5	59.1	37.7	27.8	175.7	703.3
1956 [a]								752.4
1957 [a]								804.0

[a] Figures collected by author.

applications in agriculture could conceivably reach 100-200 million lb by 1960. If several such volume new developments are realized, the vinyls will almost certainly reach one billion pounds in 1960.

Some idea of the amazing versatility of the vinyls may be had from another forecast for 1960 consumption of PVC which states that coated fabrics applications in 1960 will approximate 50 million lb, slush molding 60 million, coated glass 8, vinyl foams 25, and cast film 3-5 million. This would total 146 million lb by 1960. Such a figure of 25 million lb of plastisol resin for foam applications will be considered pessimistic by some observers who predict several times this amount by 1960. However, the use of polyvinyl chloride in foam applications in 1957 is relatively small, probably not exceeding five million pounds. More optimistic surveys estimate 1960 vinyl foam output at 125 million lb or more. On a volume basis, PVC foam is slightly cheaper than latex foam. S.P.I. estimates for vinyl foam in 1960 are 75 million lb, mainly in flexible foam materials.

It is believed that one of the major potential growth pictures for polyvinyl chloride in the United States lies in the general field of rigid applications. Rigid PVC in valves, pipe, and fittings has not progressed in the United States as much as in Europe. An indication of the anticipated growth rate of rigid PVC in the United States is exemplified by several major producers of metal pipe entering the field of rigid PVC pipe production. It is expected that rigid polyvinyl chloride will also enter present day use applications of polystyrene, polyethylene, cellulose acetate, cellulose acetate-butyrate, and other resins. A major outlet has recently seen the installation of rigid PVC pipe in ships of the U. S. Navy wherein the pipe is used to transport sea water to wash down ships in the case of atomic attack. Some of the more optimistic producers of rigid PVC predict a growth in this country to 200 million lb by 1960. A figure of 50 million lb is in prospect and 100 million lb is not entirely unreasonable.

Another rapidly growing application involves the use of PVC in electrical wire and cable, estimated at 50 million lb for 1952. This is believed to have been more than doubled in 1957 in that the wiring of new homes is reported to use over 90 and probably as much as 95% vinyl-coated wire. This PVC application is almost entirely a suspension grade, high molecular weight homopolymer. The majority of these polymers are easy-processing. The present day limit is in 105°C wire applications, but this is expected to be increased in the near future.

This growth potential of PVC is indicated in that the 1957 use of rubber in wire coatings is perhaps still 125 million lb.

A large electrical user of PVC has indicated privately that he expects 1960 purchase of PVC by the wire and cable industry to reach 150 million lb with 175 million lb not unlikely.

Recent major applications have increased the consumption of vinyl film materially above production figures of 1950 which were approximately 80 million lb. It is anticipated that film uses will reach an estimated 150 million lb by 1960. This is a conservative estimate, and if some of the agricultural predictions are fulfilled, the 1960 total will far outstrip this amount.

Whereas high molecular weight resins are generally used in calendered film, sheeting applications require lower molecular weight. Sheeting manufactured in 1956 was approximately 65 million lb. This material is mostly consumed in highly plasticized formulations, although perhaps 10-15 million lb is used in rigid applications. Despite large volume use in luggage in particular, it is generally believed that the growth pattern of vinyl sheeting will not be as great as film. Clear rigid sheeting can be made from vinyl chloride-vinyl acetate copolymer, and this application in 1957 required perhaps 10-15 million lb of resin. Rigid, non-plasticized sheets are produced from low molecular weight, easy-processing homopolymers as opaque compositions. This sale in 1957 is estimated at 8 to 10 million lb. An estimated production of rigid vinyl sheeting in 1960 is 75 million lb and in excess of 100 million lb possible.

Virtually all vinyl film is calendered. A small amount (3-5 million lb in 1957) is cast from solution. There is also a small amount of vinyl film which is extruded and blown. This material was made by two United States manufacturers in 1957. This thin gauge (approximately 1 mil film) has been characterized in the past by surface imperfections. It is possible that attempts to improve extrusion conditions and equipment will permit such thin gauge film to be produced more satisfactorily in the near future. Thin gauged vinyl film, 1 mil or less, could enjoy a rather marked sale in both plasticized and rigid applications. It is reported that calenders were being produced in Germany in 1957 which enable vinyl film to be calendered in 1 mil thickness and free of surface imperfections and pin holes.

Extrusion of shapes and profiles uses mainly high molecular weight suspension homopolymer of PVC. Various weltings for the automotive and shoe industry, window channeling, basket material, extruded tubing, etc., totaled perhaps 45 million lb in 1957. A relatively new, large volume application is extrusion of PVC disposable surgical tubing. This particular extrusion poses a somewhat different problem to the fabricator in that non-toxic plasticizers and stabilizers must be used. In addition, surgical tubing requires heavy metal ions to be absent in the polymer or at a very minimum. This broad category of profile extrusion is expected to grow to about 75-100 million lb by 1960.

A somewhat similar type of PVC extrusion is garden hose. This is also a steadily growing market, and this application in 1957 approximates 25 million lb of resin. The garden hose market is another example where the vinyls have crowded other materials to a large degree off the market. It is believed that the total garden hose volume today is about 75% PVC, the remainder being mostly rubber.

Slush moldings are made of dispersion resins in various plastisol formulations. This business is primarily confined to toys and novelty trade. It is estimated that the total volume of resin in slush molding applications in 1957 was 20 million lb with a growth potential in 1960 to perhaps 60 million lb.

Moldings, other than slush moldings, are generally made of medium to low molecular weight easy-processing homopolymers. The vast number of items fabricated by such a technique is roughly the same volume as that of slush moldings. The future trend in these applications is most uncertain, as no obvious pattern can be detected. It is logical that modest growth potential exists in such moldings and perhaps this volume will reach 35-40 million lb in 1960.

An accelerating sale of vinyls is for phonograph records. These resins are copolymers of vinyl chloride and vinyl acetate. Growth in this application will possibly reach 35 million lb by 1960, as 1957 saw 20-25 million lb so converted.

The 1956 estimate from a private source for molding and extrusion is 200 million lb of PVC resin. The approximate distribution was 100 million lb for electric wire and cable, 25,000,000 for extruded profiles, 25,000,000 in garden hose, 15,000,000 for slush moldings, 20,000,000 for other moldings and rigid applications, and 15,000,000 for phonograph records.

A reasonably conservative estimate for the production of vinyl chloride and its copolymers in the United States by 1960 is as follows: suspension homopolymers, 500-600,000,000 lb; copolymers, 165-210,000,000 lb; dispersion polymers, 75-100,000,000 lb.

The estimated total vinyl monomer capacity of the ten producers in 1957 is 930,000,000 lb per annum. The two newest producers, Allied Chemical and Ethyl Corporation, do not at this writing produce the polymer. These data are given in Table 1.8.

The contract price, FOB plant in tank car quantities for vinyl chloride monomer in early 1957 is reported to be in the 10.5-11.2-cent per pound price range. Dow announced in June, 1957, a price increase to 12.5 cents, tank cars, FOB, Freeport, Texas, (non-contract). It is anticipated that this contract monomer price will not greatly exceed 12 cents per lb by 1960 and possibly will drop below the 10.5-cent figure.

The last available export data on vinyls is incorporated in the Bureau of the Census Report No. ST410 for the year 1955. Vinyl chloride and copolymer uncompounded resins

TABLE 1.8. ESTIMATED VINYL MONOMER CAPACITY (1957)
(000,000 #)

	Company	Amount	Location
1.	Allied Chemical (Solvay)	80	Moundsville, W. Va.
2.	Bakelite	200	S. Charleston, W. Va.; Tex. City, Tex.
3.	Diamond	50	Deer Park, Tex.
4.	Dow	100	Midland, Mich.; Freeport, Tex.
5.	Ethyl Corp.	60	Baton Rouge, La.
6.	General Tire	40	Ashtabula, Ohio
7.	Goodrich	240	Niagara Falls, N. Y.; Louisville, Calvert City, Ky.
8.	Goodyear	40	Niagara Falls, N. Y.
9.	Monsanto	105	Texas City, Tex.
10.	Naugatuck (U. S. Rubber)	55	Painesville, Ohio
	Grand Total	970	

exported were 35 million lb and compounded, 15 million lb.
Similar figures for 1957 were expected. The United Kingdom
was the largest exporter with 13.5 million lb. An unusual
factor is that Italy ranked seventh among importers with over
one-half million lb of the homopolymer, although that country
was also the largest exporter of vinyl resins to the United
States.

Despite the price reductions in 1956 in this country to
27 cents per lb,* considerable import of polyvinyl chloride
from abroad still exists. The import duty on this foreign PVC
is 15% ad valorem plus 3 cents per lb for a total of approximately 7.5 cents. The total purchase of imported PVC in
this country for 1957 is expected to be in the range of 30-35
million lb, although Department of Commerce preliminary
figures on resin imports for 1956 were set at around 60 million lb.

One authority states that the total productive capacity of

* Effective June, 1958, the carload price was 25 cents per lb.

PVC in Europe is approximately 90,000 metric tons a year in Germany, 65,000 in England, and 45,000 tons in Italy. This capacity by companies is indicated in Table 1.9.

TABLE 1.9. PVC RESIN CAPACITIES IN EUROPE

Metric Tons

Germany

Chemische Werke Huels	35,000
Wacker Chemie Gmbh	25,000
Badische Aniline	15,000
Farbrverke Hoechst	10,000
Anorgana	2,500
Dynamit A. G.	2,500

England

I.C.I.	30,000
British Geon	30,000
Bakelite	5,000

Italy

Montecatini	26,000
Sicedison	12,000
Solvic	7,000

France

Pechiney	20,000
Solvic	12,000-25,000
St. Gobain	12,000
Rhone-Poulenc	4,000
Kuhlmann	1,000

Solvic, *Belgium*	15,000
Shell, *Holland*	3,000
Lonza, *Switzerland*	5,000
Stockholm Superphosphate, *Sweden*	7,000
Heroya, *Norway*	5,000

The present domestic use of PVC in Italy is believed to be about 15,000 metric tons. This permits some export which is largely to the United States.

The present capacity of Solvic production in Belgium, France, Austria, Italy, Spain and Brazil is believed to be 30,000 metric tons with expected expanded capacity to reach a total of about 60,000 metric tons. It is also possible that Solvic uses processes of I.C.I.

Present Japanese PVC manufacturing facilities are estimated at 35,000 tons with expansion possibilities to about 50,000 tons by 1960. Fair to poor quality Japanese resin is being exported in increasing amounts to the United States.

A well qualified United States consultant reports that a European producer estimates the world PVC consumption in 1955 at 535,000 metric tons, 240,000 of this in the United States, 210,000 for the rest of the Free World, and 85,000 tons in the Communist-dominated countries. It is equally interesting that this same European observer predicts by 1965 that the rest of the Free World, exclusive of the Communist countries, will use almost twice as much PVC as the United States and that the gross world consumption will in that year approximate 1.3 million metric tons.

In Table 1.10, data are presented to indicate the price structure of PVC homopolymer from January 1, 1940 to March 1, 1958. In 1940, the F.O.B. plant price in carload lots of 30,000 lb or more was 48 cents. In 1948, the delivered price in the same quantities was 34 cents, while the January 9, 1956 delivered price in truckload lots of 20,000 lb or more was 27 cents.

A 1957 estimate of production figures of polyvinyl alcohol, butyral and acetal and the homo- and copolymers of polyvinyl acetate are given in Table 1.11. This estimate totals 140 million lb for the above described types and a polyvinyl acetate homopolymer use of 55 million lb. This latter quantity is believed to be perhaps some 5-10 million lb larger for 1957. Table 1.2 preliminary United States Tariff Commission reports for 1957 indicate this total to be 154.5 million lb.

TABLE 1.10. PRICES PVC RESIN *

(Homopolymer and 95/5 Vinyl chloride/Vinyl Acetate)

F.O.B. Plant

January 1, 1940	48¢	Carload 30,000 lb or more
March 15, 1943	45¢	Carload 30,000 lb or more
December 1, 1943	42¢	Carload 30,000 lb or more
May 15, 1944	40¢	Carload 30,000 lb or more
September 1, 1944	38¢	Carload 30,000 lb or more
April 10, 1945	35¢	Carload 30,000 lb or more
December 10, 1945	33¢	Carload 30,000 lb or more

Delivered Price

September 15, 1948	34¢	Carload 30,000 lb or more
September 15, 1950	36¢	Carload 30,000 lb or more
December 13, 1950	38¢	Carload 30,000 lb or more

Delivered Price

Truckload 20,000 lb or more
(depending on published
tariff rates)

March 1, 1952	38¢	,,
June 27, 1955	31¢	,,
January 9, 1956	27¢	,,
to March 1, 1958		

* Effective June, 1958, the carload price was 25 cents per lb.

TABLE 1.11. 1957 PRODUCTION

	lb
Polyvinyl alcohol	32,000,000
Polyvinyl butyral and acetal	35,000,000
Polyvinyl acetate-copolymer uses	18,000,000
Polyvinyl acetate-homopolymer uses	55,000,000
Total	140,000,000

Breakdown of Polyvinyl Acetate-Homopolymer Uses

Adhesives	30,000,000
Textile	10,000,000
Paint	10,000,000
Miscellaneous	5,000,000
	55,000,000 lb

Adhesive applications in 1957 are estimated for polyvinyl acetate to be of the order of 32-35 million lb at an average price of 35 cents a lb. Ten million lb of polyvinyl alcohol at 75 cents per lb also was used in adhesives while other vinyls in adhesives total perhaps 5 million lb at a price of 25 cents to in excess of $1.00.

Polyvinyl acetate is the intermediate in production of polyvinyl alcohol. It is apparent that some production figures list both products as end products although they actually are not. Paint latex shows great growth prospect.

The use of polyvinyl acetate as a "starch" is growing. Polyvinyl acetate emulsions as a replacement for conventional grain starch are stated to withstand as many as 15 launderings. The 1957 sale of this emulsion application approximates $10,000,000.

Vinylidene chloride use in resin in the United States is estimated at 70,000,000 lb in the finished product. Vinylidene chloride copolymerizes with many substituted ethylenes. The copolymer of vinyl chloride is the most important application, followed by acrylonitrile. The relative insolubility and intractability of polyvinylidene chloride makes applications of the homopolymer quite limited. Copolymers of vinyl chloride and vinylidene chloride (85% vinylidene chloride) were introduced by Dow Chemical Company as saran. In the extrusion of saran, special machine design is necessary to avoid plastic holdup and decomposition of the polymer. Dow supplies plasticized and stabilized formulations of the vinylidene chloride-vinyl chloride copolymer for extrusion operations. The 1957 price schedule for saran 115 in carload lots and over was 39 cents per lb in natural finishes; the colored material 49 cents per lb, while black compositions were 42 cents.

The saran polymer has been marketed in a number of different forms. Filament usage for the most part has been confined to screening and seat covering applications. This market does not appear to be growing due to a large degree to competition of the cheaper polyvinyl chloride resins. Other screening competition has arisen from vinyl coated glass. Rattan filament enjoys sale for scouring pads for use in the kitchen. This latter application is perhaps 2 million lb per year. Saran Wrap of Dow and "Cryovac" of Dewey & Almy are extruded film. The total 1957 production of these films by these two companies is estimated at 25 million lb. Other relatively minor uses of the saran type polymer are in various paper coatings, pipe applications, paint and staple fiber. The total consumption in these minor applications in 1957 probably did not exceed 8 million lb.

Dow has announced a capacity for the manufacture of 60 million rolls of Saran Wrap per year. It is suspected that their market has not reached this sale. "Cryovac" sale has exceeded expectations in some quarters. Indications are that it has a higher percentage of vinyl chloride than Saran Wrap. This is done in order to obtain greater shrinkage of the product.

From Table 1.12, it is seen that the estimated usage of the copolymer of vinylidene chloride in 1957 is 70 million lb and 107 million is predicted for 1960. Both these figures include vinylidene chloride used by Goodrich and others in comonomer applications. In some of these resins, use of vinylidene chloride is substantially less than 85%, some being 5%.

A number of relatively minor uses for other vinyl monomers and polymers exist. The most recent application involves manufacturing facilities for vinyl stearate by the Air Reduction Chemical Company. By the end of 1957, Air Reduction plans to have on stream a plant at Calvert City, Kentucky, with an annual capacity of 2 million lb of vinyl stearate. Vinyl stearate-vinyl acetate copolymers produce tough, flexible film with a high degree of water resistance and may also be used as vehicles for exterior emulsion paints, as well as uses in textile finishes, paper coatings and adhesives.

TABLE 1.12. ESTIMATED VINYLIDENE (85%)—
VINYL CHLORIDE PRODUCTION
(Million lb)

	1957	1960
Filament		
Screening	7	8
Seat cover	25	27
Scouring pads	2	2
Film		
Saran Wrap	6	20
Cryovac	19	30
Paper and other coatings	3	3
Paint	1	3
Pipe applications	1	5
Staple fiber	1	3
Other resins (less than 85% ViCl$_2$)	5	6
	70	107

Polyvinyl acetal and formal have their major outlet as tough, heat-resistant wire enamels. Polyvinyl butyral came into its own in 1938 as a safety glass inner layer. Today it also finds outlet as surface coatings. Production in 1957 of polyvinyl butyral and acetal was 35,000,000 lb. A new vinyl polymer is polyvinyl carbazole. The monomer is used as dielectric impregnant in stationary electrical assemblies. The various vinyl alkyl ethers such as methyl, ethyl, *n*-butyl and isobutyl find their major use in copolymerization systems. These ethers copolymerize with many monomers, including vinyl chloride and have their major outlet in adhesive and coating applications. The total volume is not in excess of several million lb.

A relative newcomer to the plastics world is polyvinyl pyrrolidone. This material had its first major application as a plasma extender and today has other uses in pharmaceuticals and the textile industry. The latter application could develop into a substantial volume. An estimate of 1957 production of this material is approximately 2 to 5 million lb.

Polystyrene and polyacrylonitrile are not treated in this volume, although technically they can be considered as members of the vinyl family.

2. TYPES AND PROPERTIES

Most of the principal vinyl types are described in this chapter as well as some other materials which are either unique or offer promise of volume production. Polyvinyl alcohol, polyvinyl acetate, the vinyl acetals and polymer and copolymers of vinyl chloride are discussed in some detail.

The manufacturers of acrylic fibers and the composition of these fibers are enumerated. Other data reported in tabular form describe flexible and rigid PVC, saran, general properties of suspension PVC, vinyl pyrrolidone-vinyl acetate copolymers, and acrylonitrile copolymers of vinyl pyrrolidone. Polyvinyl alcohol and acetate are extensively treated in text and tables.

Polyvinyl alcohols are prepared by partial or complete hydrolysis of polyvinyl acetate. Polyvinyl alcohol free of its acetate precursor has complete replacement of the acetate groups by hydroxyl groups. A number of different grades of polyvinyl alcohol are commercially available. The variations in properties are largely a function of molecular weight and the degree of hydrolysis. The term percent "hydrolysis" refers to the percentage of acetate groups replaced by hydroxyl groups.

A well known brand of polyvinyl alcohol is sold by duPont under the trade name of "Elvanol." The polyvinyl alcohols manufactured are of high, medium and low viscosities. This representation is indicated in Table 2.1. As can be noted from the table, the degree of hydrolysis is virtually complete in each viscosity grade, while the lowermost degree of hydroly-

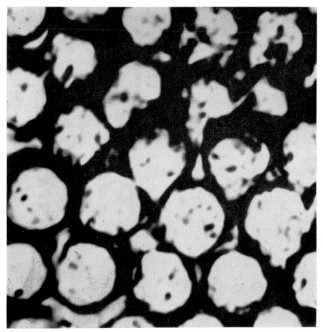

(Courtesy E. I. duPont de Nemours & Company)

Figure 2.1. Nylon multi-filament warp yarn sized with aqueous solution of polyvinyl alcohol.

sis in each grade is 86%. High viscosity PVA exhibits minimum water sensitivity, the sensitivity increasing as the degree of polymerization is decreased. Similarly, tensile strength, tear resistance, elongation and flexibility are quite good in high and medium molecular weight polymers but poor in low molecular weight materials.

TABLE 2.1. "ELVANOL" SPECIFICATIONS [1]

Grades—Code No.	Viscosity [2]	% Hydrolysis	pH	% Volatiles [3]	% Ash [4]
High Viscosity					
72-60	55-65	99-100	6-8	5	1.0
72-51	45-55	97.9-98.7	6-8	5	2.0
50-42	35-45	86-89	6-8	5	1.5
Medium Viscosity					
71-30	28-32	99-100	6-8	5	1.0
71-24	23-28	97.9-98.7	6-8	5	2.0
52-22	19-25	86-89	6-8	5	1.5
Low Viscosity					
70-05	4-6	98.5-100	6-8	5	2.0
51-05	—	87.7-89	6-8	5	1.5

[1] All specifications on dry basis except volatiles.

[2] Viscosity in centipoises of a 4% water solution at 20°C. determined by means of the Hoeppler falling ball method.

[3] Maximum.

[4] Maximum. Ash is assumed to be Na_2CO_3 and is calculated as Na_2O.

A quality of polyvinyl alcohol which permits wide applications is its property of water solubility combined with high tensile strength and tear-resistance. Water solubility allows application of a tough resin in solution form without the added cost and recovery problems found necessary by the use of organic solvents. The general properties of "Elvanol" polyvinyl alcohol are given in Table 2.2.

Water is the only practical solvent for PVA. Substantial amounts of monohydric alcohols such as methanol, ethanol and isopropanol can be added to aqueous solutions. The amount of toleration for the organic solvent added to aqueous solutions increases as the percent hydrolysis of the dissolved polyvinyl alcohol decreases. When the amount of added organic solvent exceeds the toleration limits for various

TABLE 2.2. PROPERTIES OF "ELVANOL" POLYVINYL ALCOHOL

Form	Powder
Color	White to cream
Specific gravity	1.21-1.31
Specific volume, cu in./lb	22.9-21.1
Refractive Index, n_D, 25°C.	1.49-1.53
Elongation, %, plasticized film	Up to 600
Tensile strength, psi dry, unplasticized	Up to 22,000
Hardness, Shore Durometer, plasticized	10-100
Heat-sealing temperature, °C. dry, unplasticized	165-210
Compression-molding temperature, °C. plasticized	100-150
Heat stability, °C.	Darkens slowly above 100 Darkens rapidly above 150 Decomposes above 200
Thermal coefficient of linear expansion, 0-45°C.	7×10^{-5} to 12×10^{-5}
Burning rate	Slow
Effect of light	Unaffected
Effect of strong acids	Dissolves or decomposes
Effect of strong alkalies	Softens or dissolves
Effect of weak acids	Softens or dissolves
Effect of weak alkalies	Softens or dissolves

molecular weight grades of polyvinyl alcohol, a part of the PVA is precipitated. Completely hydrolyzed grades of polymer have limited solubility in most organic compounds. Some of those compounds which are solvents are polyhydroxy materials, including ethylene glycol and other lower polyethylene glycols, glycerin and various simple alkyl amines and amides including formamide and ethanol acetamine. These particular solvents require heat to dissolve the PVA. For example, solution in glycerin requires heating to 120-150°C., gelling of the mixture occurring when the solution is cooled to room

TABLE 2.3. EFFECT OF OILS AND SOLVENTS ON "ELVANOL". PERCENT
GAIN IN WEIGHT OF MOLDED, UNPLASTICIZED "ELVANOL" IM-
MERSED FOR 10 DAYS AT 25°-35°C. (77°-95°F.)

Solvents	Grade 50-42	Grade 72-60
Alcohols		
Methanol	30.0	0.4
Ethanol, 95%	9.6	<0.1
n-butanol	<0.1	<0.1
Esters		
Ethyl acetate	<0.1	<0.1
Amyl acetate	<0.1	<0.1
Ethers		
Ethyl ether (U.S.P.)	0.1	<0.1
Ketones		
Acetone	0.2	<0.1
Hydrocarbons		
Heptane	<0.1	<0.1
Kerosene	<0.1	<0.1
Toluene	0.1	<0.1
Turpentine	0.1	<0.1
Chlorinated hydrocarbons		
Carbon tetrachloride	0.1	<0.1
Tetrachlorethane	1.0	<0.1
Ethylene dichloride	0.7	<0.1
Trichlorethylene	0.3	<0.1
Oils		
SAE #10 Oil	<0.1	<0.1
Lard oil	0.1	<0.1
Cottonseed oil	<0.1	<0.1
Raw linseed oil	<0.1	<0.1
Miscellaneous		
Oleic acid	0.9	0.9

temperature. Among the few organic solvents which will dissolve polyvinyl alcohol at room temperature are diethylenetriamine and triethylenetetramine. The effect of various solvents and oils on polyvinyl alcohol are given in Table 2.3.

Large proportions of soluble salts present in various pigments and dyes cause gelation or thickening of polyvinyl alcohol solutions. Such dyestuffs must necessarily be carefully selected to avoid the presence of these salts. A number of organic and inorganic compounds cause this gelation or precipitation of PVA from aqueous solutions. Some inorganic salts will precipitate polyvinyl alcohol from aqueous solutions when the salt is added in very low concentrations. Sodium carbonate is a very effective precipitating agent as well as borax, but the latter causes gelation instead of precipitation.

It is of interest that the well known water-immiscible plasticizers used in the plastics industry are incompatible with all grades of polyvinyl alcohol. The most widely used plasticizer is glycerin, which is compatible with partially and completely hydrolyzed PVA. Ethylene glycol and triethylene glycol also are effective plasticizers, the latter, in particular, being adapted for use with partially hydrolyzed polymer to form soft, resilient materials. Other high-boiling water-soluble organic compounds containing amide or amino groups are also serviceable plasticizers. Included in this category are formamide and ethanolamine salts such as the acetate and hydrochloride. In addition, ethanol acetamide and ethanol formamide are good plasticizers particularly for partially hydrolyzed grades.

PVA as Emulsifier

The effectiveness of PVA as an emulsifying and dispersing agent is due to its action as a surface-active agent as well as a protective colloid. In general, the dispersion-stabilizer power of PVA is good for high and medium molecular weight polymer and poor for low.

The effect on surface tension is not as great as that found with conventional wetting agents. However, lowering of the interfacial tension between oil and water phases does result. Commercial use in emulsions includes vegetable oils, plasticizers, resins, mineral oils and waxes. The partially hydrolyzed grades of PVA are generally more effective as an emulsifier than completely hydrolyzed polymer, while lower viscosity grades are less effective than high viscosity. It is also found that the addition of a small amount of a fatty alcohol sodium sulfate in conjunction with the PVA is of added value in lowering the interfacial tension. In oil and water type emulsions containing 30-50% of the dispersed phase, 2-5% PVA based on the total weight of emulsion should be used.

Price data of duPont's "Elvanol" effective in June, 1957, show the maximum price for grade 50-42, a lower price for 52-22, and the minimum price for 72-60. In 20,000 lb lots or more these costs are 88, 80 and 67 cents, respectively. It is observed from these data that the completely hydrolyzed material is the minimum price.

Other Properties

All grades of polyvinyl alcohol exhibit thermal degradation when heated in air above 212°F. Gradual discoloration, lower solubility in water and embrittlement occur. Polyvinyl alcohol film becomes yellow when heated for approximately three days at 221°F. As this temperature is increased this yellow discoloration is markedly accelerated, as two hours heating at 300°F. or 10 min. at 338°F. show similar discoloration. On the other hand, aqueous solutions of PVA can be stored for some time at boiling water temperature with no apparent change except for lowering of the pH in partially hydrolyzed grades.

All grades of PVA are considered thermoplastic, although completely hydrolyzed polymer does require the addition of considerable plasticizer before molding operations can be satisfactorily performed. It is found that higher molding temperatures are required as the percent hydrolysis increases. Heat-sealing temperatures must be increased as the percent hydrolysis of the PVA is increased.

Dielectric constants and power factors of PVA are much higher than those of other plastics commonly used as insulation materials. It is found that these properties vary greatly with changes in humidity. Samples of PVA film conditioned at 50% relative humidity show considerably higher power factor and dielectric constant than bone-dry film.

PVA films are quite stable to sunlight and artificial light. Tests on "Elvanol" films made with a carbon arc lamp and a mercury vapor lamp showed no discoloration after two weeks' exposure at a distance of two feet from the light source. Completely hydrolyzed "Elvanol" plasticized with 10% glycerin and examined at wave lengths of 2536A, 3130A and 3650A gave transmission values of 77.5, 72.9, and 81.1%, respectively. In the infrared region, the material is practically opaque from 15 microns to 6.6 microns and again at 3 microns.

The solubility of PVA polymer varies widely with the percent hydrolysis and to a somewhat lesser extent with viscosity. It is found that some cold water-soluble polymer is present in completely hydrolyzed grades, but most of the material swells and does not dissolve until the water is heated.

Solution of the highest viscosity commercial PVA is effected at about 200°F., while low-viscosity products are dissolved at a temperature 10°F. or so lower, and partially hydrolyzed grades are dissolved in either hot or cold water. Solutions of completely hydrolyzed PVA upon storing at room temperature for approximately a month show incipient gel formation. This gelation is inhibited by the addition of a proper additive such as an alkyl aryl polyether alcohol.

POLYVINYL ACETATE

Polyvinyl acetate in various forms is produced by a number of American manufacturers. Among the leading companies are Shawinigan, Dewey & Almy, duPont, Paisley Products, National Starch Products, Borden and Celanese. Polyvinyl acetate is sold in many different grades and viscosities by these manufacturers. It is much beyond the scope of this book to elucidate these individually. In general, one may state that this polymer is marketed in the general physical form of solids and emulsions.

TABLE 2.4. GELVA SOLIDS

Type	Form	Viscosity *	Softening Temp. °C.
Gelva V 1.5	Lumps	1.35-1.65	65
Gelva V 2.5	Lumps	2.25-2.75	81
Gelva V 7	Granules	6-8	106
Gelva V 15	Granules	13-17	131
Gelva V 25	Granules	22-28	153
Gelva V 60	Granules	54-66	196
Gelva V 100	Granules	90-110	
Gelva V 800	Granules	700-900	

* Viscosity in centipoises of a benzene solution containing 86 g per 1000 cc of solution, determined at 20°C., with an Ostwald viscosimeter, or equivalent.

A representative selection of polyvinyl acetate is provided by Shawinigan Resins Corporation under the trade name of "Gelva." The eight types of "Gelva" in solid form range in viscosity from 1.5 to 800 centipoises. The code number used for each type is representative of the average viscosity. This breakdown of the various solid "Gelvas" is indicated in Table 2.4 as transparent, colorless, odorless and tasteless materials. The solid polyvinyl acetates are also nontoxic and, in fact, have application in chewing gum. Light stability, heat stability and general aging characteristics are reported to be good to excellent. The densities of the resins at 20°C. are 1.19 g/cc, and the specific volume is 23.2 cu. in. per lb. The tensile strength of film varies to a maximum of about 5,000 psi.

The principal factor controlling the general properties of polyvinyl acetate is the degree of polymerization. As would be expected, the solution viscosity increases with this degree of polymerization, and this higher molecular weight is accompanied by an increase in tensile strength, softening temperature and flexibility. It is found that the tensile strength is at a maximum when the resins are dry and this property is substantially lower (200-300 psi) when the resins are wet by water. This loss of strength, however, is regained upon drying. It is of interest that even in the wet form the tensile is equal to that of good commercial paints. In that the largest use of the polymer is in the preparation of adhesives, it is noteworthy that the adhesive strength of dry coatings of polyvinyl acetate to metal, wood and glass is in the order of 1,500 psi. The shear bond strength of high viscosity resin in the dry form when measured between steel blocks is 2,000-3,000 psi.

It is observed in Table 2.4 that polyvinyl acetates do not have sharp melting points but exhibit a tendency to cold-flow at room temperature and become gradually softer as the temperature is raised.

Solubility. The solubility of polyvinyl acetate is represented in Table 2.5. These data are presented by duPont for their "Elvacet" resin. "Elvacet 60-05" is a 50% solution of resin in methanol and can be used for adhesives, coatings, and lacquer-like finishes. Films and coatings deposited from this particular solution have good water resistance, film clarity and gloss. The solutions are neutral and the resin is not degraded by the action of light and oxygen.

It is noted in Table 2.5 that the polymer is soluble in the lower alcohols, esters and ketones and insoluble in and not swollen by long chain fats, alcohols, oils or aliphatic hydrocarbons. In addition to the above described solvents it is found that anhydrous butanol, xylene and coal-tar naphtha

TABLE 2.5. SOLUBILITY OF "ELVACET" RESIN

Soluble in	Insoluble in but swelled by	Insoluble in and not swelled by
Acetic acid	Acetal	*n*-Butyl ether
Acetone	Amyl alcohol	Ethylene glycol
Acetonitrile	Amylene	Gasoline
Amyl acetate	Ethyl ether	Glycerin
Aniline	Xylene	Hexanol
Benzene		Kerosene
Butyl acetate		Linseed oil
n-Butyl alcohol (90%)		Oleic acid
Diacetone alcohol		Paraffin oil
Dioxane		Solvent naphtha
Ethyl acetate		Turpentine
Ethyl alcohol (95%)		
Ethylene dichloride		
Isopropyl acetate		
Isopropyl alcohol (90%)		
Methyl acetate		
Methyl alcohol		
Methyl ethyl ketone		
Methyl isobutyl ketone		
Nitrobenzene		
Nitromethane		
Tetrahydrofuran		
Toluene		
Trichlorethylene		

are solvents which will dissolve polyvinyl acetate when hot, and soften and swell the resin only when cold. These three solvents when hot are often used as diluents with other solvents.

Polyvinyl acetate is polymerized by any of three methods; emulsion or dispersion polymerization, bulk or block polymerization, and by solution polymerization. These techniques will be described in a later chapter, though the solution method can be mentioned at this place.

Solution polymerization is known to be commercially feasible by the use of such specific solvents as methanol, acetone, toluene, xylene and ethanol. The Borden Company supplies ten grades of polyvinyl acetate in solution under the trade name of "Polyco." These solutions are standard in solvent content, viscosity and average molecular weight, and, in general, the solids contents vary from 60 to 72%. For economy in shipping these solutions are prepared in 70% concentrations. In that some of the solutions are quite viscous and of poor flow characteristics, a 50% concentration can be more effectively handled.

All polyvinyl acetate resins absorb small percentages of water upon prolonged immersion and thus acquire a milky blush which disappears upon drying. These resins have behavior somewhat characteristic to that of stable, high molecular weight organic esters. The acetate is hydrolyzed by both strong alkalies and acids, this hydrolysis becoming marked at elevated temperatures. The resins are thermoplastic but do not have sharp melting points and show progressive softening as the temperature is elevated. Cold flow is particularly evident with low molecular weight grades particularly when plasticizers, solvents or moisture are present. As can be expected, compounding can reduce this difficulty.

Chemical Resistance. The chemical resistance of polyvinyl acetate, while not superior, does offer certain advantages. The resin cannot be recommended as a coating which must resist strong alkali, but in various protective coatings the resins are of interest in covering plaster, cement and other mildly alkaline surfaces. The polyvinyl acetates are highly resistant to salt spray, and as a paint coating are at least equal to nitrocellulose lacquers and varnishes. These resins have good chemical resistance to the action of corrosive gases such as chlorine and also offer good protection against sulfide tarnish on silver. Resistance to various petroleum fractions, oils and greases is also characteristic.

Polyvinyl acetate resins do degrade thermally, the depolymerization being rapid above 150°C. In general, these resins can withstand heating at 130°C. for approximately 24 hr without marked change in color, while fall-off in properties is not great up to several hours' exposure at 200°C. If heating is prolonged at 150-170°C. beyond a 24-hr period, the resin gradually darkens, but otherwise the properties remain virtually unchanged. When the temperature is further elevated to in excess of 200°C., very vigorous thermal decomposition occurs and the resin becomes dark and insoluble. It has been reported that this property is of some importance in the electrical field, as these resins are less likely to form a conducting carbon track in an arc as is common in many resinous materials. It is generally true that polyvinyl acetates are flexible independent of viscosity (molecular weight) in the approximate temperature range of 45-50°C.

The moisture vapor permeability of polyvinyl acetate is approximately 250 when compared to moistureproof cellophane taken as unity. This is slightly more moistureproof than non-moistureproof cellophane. This characteristic is useful in primers for application in wood and paper where the absorption of moisture causes swelling of the base. The film being plasticized by moisture does not crack or peel, and lacquers of this resin have been successfully applied over damp wood without injury to the film as the wood becomes dry.

Polyvinyl acetate is combustible when a sheet is ignited at the bottom and as long as the plastic is subjected to the heat of a flame. In this sense the combustibility is comparable to cellulose acetate. When flammable solvents are used in the preparation of films this tendency is greater than when compounding is with non-flammable materials.

Vinyl Acetate Polymers Versus Copolymers. Low molecular weight polymers of vinyl acetate exhibit soft, resinous properties, but are brittle at low temperatures. Higher molecular weight polymer shows a less marked sensitivity to impact as well as higher softening temperatures. Since certain commercial applications require a quite flexible polymer, some

TABLE 2.6. DAREX

Product	Special Features	Total Solids %	Wet Lb Per Gal.	Viscosity Cps.
Polymers				
52L	Medium molecular weight; low viscosity	54-56	9.1	300-600
56L	High molecular weight; Low viscosity	54-56	9.1	300-600
59L	Medium molecular weight; high viscosity	54-56	9.1	1000-1200
Copolymers				
61L	High viscosity; medium molecular weight; Superior water resistance; borax compatibility	54-56	9.2	2000-4000
"Everflex A"	Permanently flexible films	54-56	9.0	1000-1400
"Everflex B"	Permanently flexible films (more flexible than Everflex A)	54-56	9.0	1000-1400
"Everflex G"	Permanently flexible films; Superior water resistance	50-52	8.9	300-600
"Polymer Y"	Low viscosity; Aqueous solution; Alkali soluble films	38-40	8.9	100-500

* Determined by pressing together two coated sheets of Kraft paper face to face

manufacturers have turned to copolymers. Dewey & Almy manufacture both polymers and copolymers of vinyl acetate under the trade name of "Darex." The copolymers sold by this company as "Everflex" are probably vinyl acetate copolymerized with dibutylmaleate, although the manufacturer does not indicate the composition.

POLYVINYL ACETATE

Block-ing Temp.* °F.	Particle Size Average	Film Clarity and Gloss	Water Resist-ance	Approx-imate Molecular Wt.	Typical End Uses
150	Less than 2 microns	Good	Good	40,000	Textile sizings, adhesives, paints, coatings.
250	1 micron	Good	Good	130,000	Textile sizings, adhesives, paints, coatings.
175	Less than 3 microns	Fair	Fair	40,000	Textile sizings, adhesives, paints, coatings
130	1 micron	Good	Very Good	40,000	Same as above with special advantage of borax compatibility. Example: Fire retardant paints.
175	Less than 2 microns	Very Good	Very Good	40,000	Sizings, coatings, adhesives.
120	Less than 2 microns	Very Good	Very Good	15,000	Same as above where more flexible films are required.
130	Less than 2 microns	Excel-lent	Excel-lent	40,000	Paints, scrub-resistant coatings.
100	Colloidal Solution	Excel-lent	Excel-lent	14,000	Self polishing waxes, specialty primer sealers.

for 24 hours using pressure of 1 lb per square inch.

Such applications as paint, adhesives and textile sizings require more flexible films than are produced by the homopolymer. This degree of plasticization may be an internal one supplied by the copolymerizing monomer. In this particular brand of resin the added ingredient is unlike a typical plasticizer, as the tendency to migrate and bleed, with subsequent

loss of film flexibility, is not present. This suggests that the
"Everflexes" are true copolymers in which a second monomer
is incorporated in the polymer structure. By such means permanent film flexibility is imparted.

Table 2.6 represents the differences betwen these polymers
and copolymers. It is observed that "Darex 56-L" is reported
to be in the molecular weight range of 130,000. It is interesting that "Everflex B" copolymer is reported to be more flexible than "Everflex A," although the former has a molecular
weight of 15,000 versus 40,000 for "Everflex A." It is possible that "Everflex B" contains a larger percentage of the
copolymerizing monomer. In addition to the normal emulsions
supplied in the "Darex" line, "Polymer Y" is a colloidal water
solution of a modified polyvinyl acetate. This neutral solution
is supplied as a translucent, semi-viscous fluid which is miscible with water in all proportions. It is reported that this
polymer has high water resistance in the form of cured films,
and that the clear, glossy and hard films have use as coating
materials and as binders in coating compounds.

Polyvinyl Acetate Emulsions. Most emulsions of polyvinyl
acetate contain non-ionic protective colloids and have good
stability to mechanical agitation and to the addition of small
quantities of dilute acid or alkali. These emulsions are normally acidic, but if desired they can be made neutral or alkaline by the addition of ammonia or various amines such as
triethanolamine. It is generally desirable to keep the pH low
so that unnecessary hydrolysis of the resin does not occur
with subsequent decreased water resistance. The emulsions
are coagulated by the addition of multivalent salts. A particularly effective additive is borax, and it has been found that
even a small amount of this material present in some grades
of premixed casein is often sufficient to cause gelation.

Of real concern is the sensitivity of these polymer emulsions
and copolymer latices to freezing. These materials, if frozen,
are permanently damaged, and therefore must be protected

at all times from freezing temperatures. The emulsions are capable of settling action as differentiated from freezing; the settled polymer can readily be redispersed by simple agitation, but damage from freezing is irreversible. Unlike the true emulsions, the "Polymer Y" of Dewey & Almy is a colloidal solution and does not settle upon great dilution and its properties are not adversely affected by freezing and thawing. This would permit some applications where conventional emulsions are unsatisfactory. Freeze stability is of vital consideration to paint manufacturers.

Aqueous dispersions of polyvinyl acetate are frequently modified to provide better flexibility by incorporating as little as 5% of various plasticizers. Among the more popular plasticizers are dibutyl phthalate and tributyl phosphate, although many plasticizers are reported. In some applications as little as 2 parts plasticizer based on the polymer are used, while in others as much as 35 to 45 parts are needed to produce flexibility equivalent to nitrocellulose with 30 parts of plasticizer. The amount of the plasticizer used depends on the plasticizer itself as each has specific contributions.

In various lacquers and varnish applications, the use of polyvinyl acetate emulsions is limited by the quantity of solids capable of being carried by the solvent at workable viscosities. The viscosity of a resin emulsion is independent of the viscosity of the resin phase, but is a function of the size and nature of the dispersed particles, the characteristics of the emulsifying agents, and the water content. Dispersions of high molecular weight polymers generally provide higher solids concentration at workable viscosities rather than with solvent solutions of these same polymers. This concept, such as that employed by the Borden Company, is especially noticeable when vinyl acetate monomer is first emulsified and then polymerized in the dispersed state to produce resin dispersions. These aqueous dispersions permit porous surfaces to be uniformly coated at various film thicknesses. The aqueous portion of the dispersion can penetrate the surface, leaving the resin phase on top. Another useful property of these materials is utilized in those applications where increased penetration is desired for an unusual bonding need. In this case dispersions of finer particle size incorporated with a wetting agent are often used. Where the penetration of both water and resin must be kept at a minimum, this is accomplished by increasing the viscosity of the dispersion without increasing the solids content of the material.

The ease of application of emulsions and dispersions of polyvinyl acetate is well known, particularly the fact that they can be applied to damp or wet surfaces which would not permit more conventional paint or coating compositions to adhere. Another important property of these materials is that fire and explosion hazards are practically eliminated when these dispersions are used in place of resin or lacquer solutions. Accompanying this safety factor is the elimination of odor and toxic problems. As water is a diluent for the dispersed emulsions, the need for costly solvents is eliminated.

Addition of plasticizers to polyvinyl acetate increases flexibility, water resistance and gloss while increasing tack and adhesion. These properties are accompanied by lower softening and heat-sealing temperatures of the dried film. In most additions of plasticizer to the aqueous dispersions, the plasticizer is directly added with slight agitation. The amount of the added plasticizer varies widely and is generally used in small amounts, but as much as 150 parts of plasticizer have been used to make pressure sensitive adhesives.

Effect of Buffers and Alkalies. The presence of small quantities of acetic acid in dispersions of polyvinyl acetate results in a pH of about 4.0 to 5.0. These dispersions permit pH adjustment to the neutral point or a temporary adjustment to an alkaline state by the addition of dilute solutions of weak alkalies, such as ammonia and triethanolamine, or the addition of water-insoluble, mildly alkaline compounds such as zinc oxide or calcium carbonate. An alkaline material is added cautiously, since high local concentration of alkali can cause coagulation; addition to the dispersion is made with continuous agitation. The alkaline agent need not be in solution as magnesium oxide, zinc oxide, and calcium carbonate can be added as dry powder or as water dispersed slurries. The pH will not remain permanent when a pH above 7 is obtained by the addition of alkali.

Slow hydrolysis of the polymer results, with a subsequent drop in the pH when triethanolamine is added to the polyvinyl acetate dispersion. In addition to the usual alkaline additives, various buffer salts, such as sodium bicarbonate and disodium phosphate, can be used to elevate the pH. Care must be exercised whenever strongly ionized salts are added to these emulsions to avoid a salting-out effect. Borax is compatible with certain polyvinyl acetate dispersions, but as was mentioned previously, this compound must be handled with extreme care to avoid coagulation.

Addition of Solvents. Solvents are added to emulsions of polyvinyl acetate particularly in the manufacture of adhesives to improve water resistance, increase viscosity, increase gloss and in certain cases improve adhesion to surfaces of various plastic films, cellophane and wax paper. Low-boiling solvents improve initial tack, while specific high-boiling solvents produce a delayed tack or lower film heat-sealing temperatures. Among the more active solvents are methanol, ethanol, and isopropanol, methyl and ethyl acetate, benzene and toluene, carbon tetrachloride, methylene chloride, cellosolve, dioxan, acetone and methyl ethyl ketone. Although various diluents can be used in the presence of active solvents, these additions must be carefully regulated. Generally acceptable diluents are alcohols somewhat higher than those used as active solvents, these being butanol and methyl amyl alcohol while other diluents are methyl amyl acetate, xylene, ethyl ether, and diisobutyl ketone. Among non-solvents in addition to water are gasoline, mineral oil, glycol, glycerin and turpentine. These are presented in Table 2.7.

TABLE 2.7. SOLVENTS FOR POLYVINYL ACETATE

Active Solvents	Diluents	Non-Solvents
Alcohols		
Methanol	*n*-Butanol	Octyl alcohol
95% Ethanol	*sec.*-Butanol	Ethylene glycol
95% Isopropanol	Hexyl alcohol	Glycerin
Chlorinated Hydrocarbons		
Methylene chloride		
Carbon tetrachloride		
Chlorobenzene		
Esters		
Ethyl acetate	Methyl amyl acetate	Ethyl silicate
Isopropyl acetate	Octyl acetate	Linseed oil
Butyl acetate		
Hydrocarbons		
Benzol	Xylol	Gasoline
Toluol	"Solvesso #1"	Mineral oil
	Ethyl benzene	Naphtha
Ketones		
Acetone	Diisobutyl ketone	
Methyl ethyl ketone		
Methyl isobutyl ketone		
Diacetone alcohol		
Mesityl oxide		
Miscellaneous		
Nitroethane		Turpentine
Tetrahydrofuran		Carbon disulfide

Polyvinyl Acetate Solutions

Polyvinyl acetate solutions offer certain advantages in ease of compounding over emulsion systems. Many resins which are difficult to disperse in aqueous systems are readily compounded with polyvinyl acetate solutions. Compounding with other resins or gums can improve impact strength, water resistance, blocking temperatures, oil resistance, adhesion to non-porous surfaces, heat sealing and tackiness.

In addition to compatibility with many gums polyvinyl acetate solutions are compatible with chlorinated rubber, phenolics, nitrocellulose and cellulose acetopropionate. Partial compatibility exists with ethyl cellulose, a maximum of 10 parts of ethocel being used per hundred polyvinyl acetate. Even in solution form polyvinyl acetate is incompatible with PVC, PVC-acetate, polyvinylidene chloride, polystyrene, polyvinyl acetals, alkyds, cellulose acetate and urea-formaldehyde. In general, one finds compatibility promoted by nitro, hydroxyl, ester, carboxyl, phenolic or polychlor groups. Incompatibility is promoted by long chain paraffin hydrocarbons.

Copolymers of Vinyl Acetate

It has been reported that a copolymer with acrylonitrile and vinyl acetate permits compression-molding which when the specimens are homogeneous, have tensile strengths of 8300 psi and flexural strengths of 15600 psi. These copolymers contain as much as 55% vinyl acetate. A three-component system of vinyl acetate, acrylonitrile, and methacrylonitrile has good heat resistance, hardness, and exceptional flexibility. The material may be cast, extruded, and injection or compression-molded. This permits exposure of the material to relatively high temperatures without decomposition.

The very important copolymer, vinyl chloride, will be described elsewhere.

POLYVINYL ACETALS

The general term "polyvinyl acetal" refers to polymers formed by partial or nearly complete replacement of the hydroxyl groups of polyvinyl alcohol with aldehydes. These

materials are derived from polyvinyl acetate which is hydrolyzed by various agents; the free hydroxyl groups are then
reacted with aldehydes or a reactive carbonyl group to form
acetal groups. A wide variety of resins can thus be formed.
Perhaps the earliest work in this field was by Shawinigan
Chemicals Ltd. about 1929.

The factors which govern the properties of a given polyvinyl acetal resin are many. Perhaps the most important are:
the molecular weight of the polyvinyl acetate used; the choice
of aldehyde; the extent of hydrolysis of the polyvinyl acetate
which, of course, governs the percentage of the acetyl groups
replaced by hydroxyl groups; and lastly the percentage of
these hydroxyl groups which are replaced by aldehyde groups.
Such a wide variation of these conditions is possible that one
may prepare resins of greatly different properties to suit
individual applications. It is thus possible to produce polyvinyl acetals of a wide variation in tensile and impact strengths,
solubility, hardness, solution viscosity (molecular weight),
softening temperatures and dimensional stability. If one were
to use a polyvinyl acetate of low viscosity, it is observed that
the resulting polyvinyl acetals are of lower softening temperatures, tensile and impact strengths and resin hardness. By the
same token higher molecular weight polyvinyl acetates tend
to increase these physical properties.

The solubilities of polyvinyl acetals are markedly affected
by varying the percentage of the acetal reaction. In lower-
membered aldehydes replacement of a relatively low percentage of hydroxyl groups by acetal results in water solubility
of the resin, but as the percentage acetal reaction is increased
the resins become alcohol-soluble, then acetone-soluble at
higher acetal levels, and when the percentage acetal reaction
approaches 90% solubility is in non-polar solvents, such as
benzene. By carefully controlling reaction conditions the percentage acetal reaction can be varied from a low value to
essentially complete reaction. As is characteristic of condensa-

tion reactions, it is not believed that 100% acetal reaction is commercially achieved.

Polyvinyl Formal

Polyvinyl formal produced by Shawinigan is trade marked "Formvar." The most extensive use of this material is in the manufacture of tough, heat-resistant wire enamel. These materials are white to straw-colored, free-flowing powders which have a maximum grain size of 12 mesh. Films produced from this material are transparent with an amber cast. All the "Formvars" are believed to be prepared by the simultaneous hydrolysis and acetylization of polyvinyl acetate. The first digits of the grade designations in Table 2.8 are the approximate viscosities of the "Gelva" (polyvinyl acetate) used in the acetal preparation; the second digits indicate the extent to which the acetate groups have been replaced by hydrolysis. Each type of resin is available with two grades of thermal stabilization, "E" indicating a volatile stabilizer at elevated temperatures, and "S" indicates a non-volatile stabilizer.

Type 15/95 is a high viscosity material of very limited solubility which has application in magnetic wire enamel and metal-to-metal adhesives. Type 12/85 is of medium viscosity and limited solubility and is used in metal finishing. "Formvar" 7/95 is of medium viscosity and is used as a molding powder while 7/70, low viscosity material of a wide degree of solubility is also used in metal finishes. All the polyvinyl formals described in Table 2.8 are tough, rigid and dimensionally stable resins resistant to oils and with good electrical properties. The tensile strength, modulus of elasticity and flexural modulus are not affected by variations in molecular weight. The elongation at break is significantly different only in the case of the lowest molecular weight product, type 7/70. As would be expected, polyvinyl formal is less rubber-like than higher-membered alkyl aldehydes used in preparation of

TABLE 2.8. PROPERTIES

Property	Units	Method
Chemical		
Polyvinyl alcohol content	%	S [a]
Polyvinyl acetate content	%	S
Volatile content (as packed)	%	S
Viscosity	cp	S
Specific gravity	—	D792-44T
Water absorption (24 hr)	%	D570-42
Mechanical		
Tensile strength, yield	lb/in^2	D638-49T
break	lb/in^2	D638-49T
Elongation, yield	%	D638-49T
break	%	D638-49T
Modulus of elasticity (apparent)	lb/in^2	D638-49T
Flexural strength (fiber stress)	lb/in^2	D790-49T
Deflection, yield	%	D790-49T
break	%	D790-49T
Flexural modulus (E) (apparent)	lb/in^2	D790-49T
Hardness, Rockwell [b]	—	D785-48T
Impact strength, notched Izod, ½ × ½ [b]	ft/lb/in	D256-43T
notched Izod, ½ × ⅛ [c]	ft/lb/in	D256-43T
unnotched	ft/lb/in	D256-43T
Thermal		
Thermal expansion, linear	in/in/°C.	D696-44
Heat distortion temperature	°C.	D648-45T
Inflection (transition) temperature	°C.	D1043-49T
Deformation under 4000 psi load, 50°C.	%	D621-48T
70°C.	%	D621-48T
Flow temperature, 1500 psi	°C.	D569-48
Electrical		
Dielectric strength	v/mil	D149-44
Dielectric constant, 60 cps	—	D150-47T
10^3 cps	—	D150-47T
10^6 cps		
Dissipation factor, 60 cps	—	D150-47T
10^3 cps	—	D150-47T
10^6 cps	—	D150-47T

[a] Tests have been performed by A.S.T.M. methods unless otherwise indicated, at Corp. laboratories; polyvinyl alcohol by acetylation, polyvinyl acetate by hydrolysis, chloride at 20°C.

[b] Compression molded.

[c] Injection molded.

15/95E	15/95S	7/95S	12/85	7/70
5-6	7-9	7-9	5-7	5-7
9.5-13	9.5-13	9.5-13	20-27	40-50
1.0	1.5	1.5	1.5	1.5
40-60	40-60	15-22	18-22	8-10
1.2	1.2	1.2	1.2	1.2
0.75	1.1	1.1	1.5	1.5
$9\text{-}11 \times 10^3$	$9\text{-}11 \times 10^3$	$9\text{-}11 \times 10^3$	$9\text{-}11 \times 10^3$	$9\text{-}11 \times 10^3$
$9\text{-}11 \times 10^3$	$10\text{-}12 \times 10^3$	$10\text{-}12 \times 10^3$	$8\text{-}10 \times 10^3$	$5\text{-}7 \times 10^3$
4	4	4	4	3
60	70	70	60	90
$5\text{-}7 \times 10^5$	$5\text{-}7 \times 10^5$	$5\text{-}7 \times 10^5$	$5\text{-}7 \times 10^5$	$5\text{-}7 \times 10^5$
18,000	17,000	17,000	15,000	13,000
50-60	50-60	50-60	—	—
—	—	—	30-40	20-30
$5\text{-}6 \times 10^5$	$5\text{-}6 \times 10^5$	$5\text{-}6 \times 10^5$	$5\text{-}6 \times 10^5$	$5\text{-}6 \times 10^5$
M80-90	—	—	—	—
1.2-2	1.2-2	1-1.4	0.5-0.7	0.4-0.6
—	—	1.3-2.0	—	0.4-0.6
>60	>60	>60	—	—
7.7×10^5	—	—	—	—
86-92	84-92	84-92	74-80	50-60
103-107	103-107	103-107	92-96	75-80
0.2-0.4	0.2-0.4	0.2-0.4	4-6	—
1-3	1-3	1-3	—	—
160-170	160-170	140-145	145-150	—
860-1000	—	—	—	—
3.6	—	—	—	—
3.3	—	—	—	—
0.007	—	—	—	—
0.01	—	—	—	—
0.02	—	—	—	—

23°C. and 50% relative humidity. "S" refers to methods used by Shawinigan Resins
volatile at 105°C. in 1 hr and viscosity of 5 g resin made to 100 ml with ethylene

the acetals; this also results in higher softening temperature for the formal. Wire coatings of "Formvar" are normally applied by solution coating of wire. The solution contains a small amount of a phenolic resin used as a cross-linking material.

All the "Formvars" are insoluble in lower alcohols and all hydrocarbons; they are soluble in acetic acid, a 30/70 alcohol/toluene mixture, chloroform, dichloroethyl ether, dioxan, ethylene bromide and chloride, furfural, nitrobenzene and tetrachloroethane.

"Formvar" molding powders are used in injection molding applications to produce a range of molding temperatures and impact strength. These properties are indicated in Table 2.9. These compounds have a hard surface and offer good abrasion resistance and machinability.

TABLE 2.9. "FORMVAR" MOLDING POWDERS

Property	9011	9200	9300
Molding quality	Excellent	Good	Fair
Injection temperature, °F.	360-380	400-420	400-450
Injection pressure psi	18-20,000	20-25,000	20-35,000
Shrinkage, in./in.	.002-.004	.002-.004	.002-.004
Impact strength, Notched Izod ft lb/in. notch	.6-1.0	1-2	8-20
Heat distortion temperature, °F.	167°-177°	183°-197°	176°-186°
Flow temperature, 1500 psi °F.	270°-280°	284°-293°	280°-290°

Polyvinyl Butyral

Vinyl acetate monomer was first described in the literature in a German patent issued in 1912, in which the monomer was made from acetylene and acetic acid. Vinyl acetate was converted to the polymer and in 1927 a method of hydrolysis of the polyvinyl acetate to polyvinyl alcohol was developed. In the early 1930's polyvinyl alcohol was reacted with butyraldehyde and the resulting product had its first major outlet in 1938 as the interlayer in safety glass.

PVB has good resistance to alkali, sunlight, vegetable oils, greases and water. The resistance to most inorganic acids is poor. Film is not attacked by aliphatic hydrocarbons. Alcohols are the best solvents for PVB although cyclic ethers; some ketones and esters and cellosolve are also solvents. Due to the balance of hydrophilic vinyl alcohol groups and the organophilic vinyl butyral groups in the molecule, the polymer is often more soluble in mixed solvents than in any one individual solvent. It is found that water effectively decreases the viscosity of solvent mixtures. PVB dissolved in anhydrous alcohol is more soluble when a small portion of water is added to the alcohol. Vinyl butyral resins are compatible with a number of plasticizers. Raw castor oil is also compatible, but tends to soften the film without developing elasticity. The polymer is compatible with many natural resins, some phenolic resins, and a few oils. Compatibility with nitrocellulose and urea-formaldehyde resins is limited.

As PVB contains free hydroxyl groups, the resin may be made insoluble by chemical reactivity with both resinous materials (e.g., urea-formaldehyde and phenolics) and chemical agents. Water resistance is improved by baking at 275°F. when equal parts of phenolic and PVB resins are used. Flexibility is improved with increased quantities of the vinyl butyral resin. As the ratio of phenolic resin to PVB is increased, solvent resistance also increases.

Excellent impact strength and tenacious adhesion to glass are responsible for the success of polyvinyl butyral. These properties must be retained at wide variations in temperature. The film must also not develop color or opacity after long exposure to intense sunlight. The bond of the PVB to glass must hold whether it be wet or dry, and after many cycles of such.

PVB is actually a partial butyral of polyvinyl alcohol, and some unreacted polyvinyl alcohol groups are retained in the polymer. This presence of PVA contributes to some of the desirable properties of the resins. The Bakelite Company markets two polyvinyl butyral resins under the designations XYHL and XYSG which are chemically similar but differ in average molecular weight. Type XYHL is of medium molecular weight having an intrinsic viscosity of 0.81, while type XYSG yields more viscous solutions and has an intrinsic viscosity of 1.16.

(Courtesy E. I. duPont de Nemours & Company)

Figure 2.2. Laboratory test demonstration of polyvinyl butyral.

Vinyl butyral resins are characterized by their excellent adhesion to a wide variety of non-porous surfaces such as glass, metal, phenolic resins and cellulosic materials. The resins when immersed readily absorb 5-8% water and thus become softer, though prolonged immersion does not increase the water absorption, nor is the resin degraded. Compounds based on unmodified vinyl butyral resins are rarely applicable for exterior exposure, usually chalking as a result of water absorption. However, unstabilized PVB does not discolor after heating for several hours at 200°F.; but at higher temperatures the resins become amber in color and prolonged heating results in loss of alcohol solubility and the polymer becomes more soluble in hydrocarbons.

Monsanto offers to the industrial finish formulator four grades of "Butvar" varying in insolubility or in polyvinyl alcohol content. Properties of these materials are described in Table 2.10.

"Butacite" PVB sheet is supplied by duPont. This material is a soft, pliable sheeting with embossed surface dusted with finely divided sodium bicarbonate to prevent self-sticking, and

TABLE 2.10. PROPERTIES OF "BUTVAR" COATING RESINS

	"Butvar B-72A"	"Butvar B-73"	"Butvar B-76-1"	"Butvar B-90"
Hydroxyl content, % *	17.9-19.8	17.5-21.0	10.5-13.0	18.0-20.0
Polyvinyl acetate, % Max.	2.5	2.5	1.5	1.0
Viscosity, 6% in methanol @ 20°C., cps	—	—	—	13-18
Viscosity, 7½% in methanol @ 20°C., cps	140-220	40-90	—	25-35
Viscosity, 5% in ethanol @ 25°C., cps	50-85	*ca.* 35	18-28	*ca.* 22
Viscosity, 10% in ethanol @ 25°C., cps	—	*ca.* 402	*ca.* 176	*ca.* 196
Viscosity, 10% in butanol @ 25°C., cps	—	*ca.* 1215	*ca.* 348	*ca.* 456
Viscosity, 10% in Toluene-butanol @ 25°C., cps	—	*ca.* 924	*ca.* 116	*ca.* 206

* Calculated as percent polyvinyl alcohol
cps. = centipoises
1. "Butvar B-90" conforms to Type 11 Resin in MIL-C-15328A specification.
2. "Butvar B-76-1" conforms to Type 11 Resin in MIL-C-15328A specification.

Solvents

	"Butvar B-73"	"Butvar B-76-1"	"Butvar B-90"		"Butvar B-73"	"Butvar B-76-1"	"Butvar B-90"
Acetic acid	S	S	S	Ethyl			
Acetone	SW	S	SW	cellosolve	S	S	S
Butanol	S	S	S	Ethylene glycol	1	1	1
Butyl acetate,				Isophorone	S	S	S
98%	PS	S	PS	Isopropanol			
Carbon				(anhydrous)	S	S	S
tetrachloride	SW	SW	SW	Methanol	S	PS	S
Cyclohexanone	PS	S	PS	Methyl isobutyl			
Diacetone				ketone	PS	S	PS
alcohol	S	S	S	Petroleum			
Diisobutyl				naphtha	1	SW	1
ketone	SW	S	SW	Propylene			
Dioxane	S	S	S	dichloride	PS	S	PS
Ethanol, 95%	S	S	S	Toluene	SW	S	SW
Ethyl acetate,				Xylene,			
99%	SW	S	SW	coal tar	PS	PS	PS
Ethyl acetate,				Xylene,			
85%	S	S	S	petroleum	PS	PS	PS

S = Soluble
PS = Partially soluble
SW = Swells only
1 = No dissolved material
Tests made as 10% solutions by weight, with 24 hour cold agitation.

is supplied in thicknesses from .015 to .030-in., and in widths up to 46 in. This material is used in various forms of laminated constructions.

VINYL-ACRYLONITRILE POLYMERS

The acrylic fibers have enjoyed considerable sale, and in 1956 these fibers consumed about 60% of all acrylonitrile produced. These polymers will be discussed here not because of the acrylonitrile used but because of the various copolymerizing vinyl monomers. Of the approximately 125 million lb of acrylonitrile produced in the United States in 1956 only about 11 million lb was used in true plastics applications, 33 million in rubber and 76 million in fibers. Miscellaneous applications consumed an additional 5 million lb.

In the production of fibers acrylonitrile is copolymerized with relatively minor amounts of monomers, such as vinyl acetate, vinyl pyrrolidone, methyl vinyl pyridine, vinyl pyridine or vinyl chloride. These monomers improve the dyeability and probably other properties of the finished fibers. "Zefran," when it comes on stream in 1958, is expected to be produced by a relatively new technique with vinyl pyrrolidone graft polymerized onto essentially polyacrylonitrile.

TABLE 2.11. ACRYLIC FIBERS AND PRODUCERS

Fiber	Probable Composition	Producer
"Orlon"	Acrylonitrile and small amount of methyl acrylate	DuPont, Camden, S. C. (and Waynesboro, Va., late 1951)
"Acrilan"	Acrylonitrile and minor amounts of vinyl acetate and methylvinyl pyridine	Chemstrand, Decatur, Ala. (Monsanto-American Viscose)
"Creslan" (1958)	Acrylonitrile and minor amounts of vinyl acetate and methylvinyl pyridine	Cyanamid, Pensacola, Fla.
"Zefran" (1958)	85% acrylonitrile 15% vinyl pyrrolidone	Dow, Lee Hall, Va.
"Verel" (late 1956)	60% acrylonitrile 40% vinyl chloride	Tennessee Eastman Kingsport, Tenn.
"Dynel"	40% acrylonitrile 60% vinyl chloride	Carbide, South Charleston, W. Va.

Table 2.11 illustrates the acrylic fibers and their producers as well as the probable composition of the fibers.

Since copolymers which contain large proportions of polyacrylonitrile are essentially infusable and intractable, the various fibers are prepared by extrusion of a copolymer into a precipitating bath. Solvents used are dimethylformamide ("Orlon" and probably "Acrilan"), sodium thiocyanate

("Creslan") and zinc chloride ("Zefran"). Dimethyl sulfoxide and various alkylene carbonates are also under consideration as solvents. It is believed that "Verel" and "Dynel" fibers are produced by melt spinning techniques since these polymers readily melt as a result of their high percentage of vinyl chloride.

Polyvinyl chloride-nitrile rubber blends are of considerable interest in rigid vinyl applications. In general, nitrile rubber—which is often a high styrene-acrylo rubber—acts as a plasticizer when blended with polyvinyl chloride and in so doing functions as an extrusion aid. The relative proportions of the N-rubber and PVC vary widely depending upon the application. Most rigid pipe applications do not use more than 20% N-type rubber on the basis of the polyvinyl chloride content. The incorporation of the nitrile rubber materially increases the impact resistance of polyvinyl chloride, while the resin-rubber blend still exhibits the good oil and chemical resistance of the vinyl resin. Goodrich sells a mixture containing 55% PVC and 45% nitrile rubber as "Polyblend" 503, as well as "Hycar" OR-25 which contains 30% acrylo. The sale of these products is perhaps several hundred thousand pounds per year, the product being used for cable jackets and cap liners. Various latices are produced which contain 70% PVC and 30% nitrile rubber. The volume sale here is quite small but should show a gross potential in the next few years to several million pounds. The use of this latter material is as an antistick coating for paper tapes.

POLYVINYL PYRROLIDONE

General Aniline & Film operates a 30 million lb per year capacity plant at Calvert City, Kentucky, for the manufacture of polyvinyl pyrrolidone. This material is expected to be used by Dow Chemical when their acrylic fiber plant comes on stream in 1958 with "Zefran." This acrylic fiber is expected to be an 85% acrylo/15% vinylpyrrolidone polymer. In addition to this, PVP is expected to be used as a detoxifier of iodine in antiseptic and also in hair sprays as a copolymer with vinyl acetate. A number of companies are investigating the possibility of a copolymer of vinylpyrrolidone and lauryl methacrylate in lube oil additives.

PVP is prepared by a five step Reppe process starting with formaldehyde and acetylene, and had its inception during the early 1930's. When Allied investigating teams entered Germany after World War II, it was found that PVP was the chief ingredient of a widely used plasma substitute. The monomer, N-vinyl-2-pyrrolidone, is a colorless liquid of boiling point 96°C. at 14 mm, melting point 13.5°C. and of a specific gravity at 25°C. of 1.04. The monomer is stabilized with 0.1% flake sodium hydroxide, and is completely miscible with water, methanol, ethanol, ethyl acetate, ethyl ether, methylene chloride, and hydrocarbons. Vinyl pyrrolidone readily forms the homopolymer and also will copolymerize with most of the vinyl monomers including vinyl chloride, vinyl acetate, acrylonitrile, acrylic acid, maleic anhydride, N-vinylcarbazole, vinyl esters and ethers, styrene, methacrylic acid and others.

PVP is a white, amorphous powder that can be stored indefinitely. It is soluble in water as well as a wide variety of organic solvents. Dilute aqueous solutions are practically clear and colorless, but more concentrated solutions are slightly hazy and are light yellow to yellow in color. Sterilization by heating is recommended as the aqueous solutions support mold growth. This heating does not appear to damage the properties of the PVP solutions.

Copolymers

The composition of copolymers can be varied over wide limits permitting production of water-soluble or water-insoluble materials which range from viscous liquids to solids.

The water-soluble copolymers are made insoluble by heating. This insolubilization is also characteristic of the homopolymer. It is found that many copolymers have good adherence to glass, and clear films may be cast from absolute alcohol solutions of most of these materials.

Copolymers of vinylpyrrolidone and vinyl acetate may be formed in all proportions, although the rate of polymerization of vinylpyrrolidone appears to be faster than that of vinyl acetate. Polymers of high vinylpyrrolidone content are soluble in water.

The copolymer with vinyl acetate is prepared in benzene solution at reflux temperature for 6 hrs in the presence of 0.5% azodiisobutyronitrile as a catalyst. Some of the properties of the copolymer are given in Table 2.12.

Copolymers with Acrylonitrile

The acrylonitrile copolymer can be prepared in aqueous or hexane solutions with 1-2% of an azo catalyst at 50°C., in 1.5-5 hrs. This copolymer is usually a brittle solid. The specific viscosity and K value for various copolymer composi-

TABLE 2.12. VINYLPYRROLIDONE—VINYL ACETATE COPOLYMERS

% V.P.	Spec. Visc.*	K ** Value	H_2O	EtAc	Iso-propyl Alc.	EtOH MeOH	CCl_4	MEK	C_6H_6
65	0.310	34.2	S	S	S	S	I	S	S
35	0.263	31.3	I	S	Sc	S	Sc	S	S
25	0.37	37.0	I	S	Sc	S	Sc	S	S

I = Insol.
S = Sol.
c = Cloudy
* 1 gram solute per 100 ml. 2-butanone solution at 25°C.
** Fikentscher K Value

tions are presented in Table 2.13. The application of copolymerizing acrylonitrile with minor amounts of vinylpyrrolidone gives textile fibers of improved dyeability and hand.

This improvement results from the hydrophilic qualities of vinylpyrrolidone. By controlling the ratio of monomers in the copolymer, water solubility can be attained. An 85% vinylpyrrolidone-15% acrylonitrile copolymer is approximately 5% soluble in distilled water and has relatively the same solubility in methanol.

TABLE 2.13. ACRYLONITRILE COPOLYMERS

Composition of Copolymer-Wt. %		Spec. Visc.*	K **
V.P.	A.N.		
87	13	4.27	98
74.5	25.5	1.04	60
79.2	20.8	0.94	58
61.7	38.3	12.3	126
75.4	24.6	2.21	80
75.1	24.9	1.41	68
32.6	67.4	4.59	100

* 1 g of copolymer per 100 ml dimethylformamide solution at 25°C.
** Fikentscher K Value

Other Copolymers

Vinylpyrrolidone polymerized in equal weights with maleic anhydride forms light, fluffy material which is easily hydrolyzed with water or alkaline solutions to form water-soluble derivatives. If the monomer is copolymerized with isobutyl vinyl ether in a ratio of 90% vinylpyrrolidone, a water-soluble polymer results. If the vinylpyrrolidone content is decreased to 75%, the resulting copolymer is water-insoluble, thus illustrating control of hydrophilic properties by varying the vinylpyrrolidone content. This particular copolymer when cast on a glass plate from absolute ethyl alcohol deposits a nontacky film which adheres to the glass. These films are clear and water-sensitive.

POLYVINYL OXAZOLIDONE

An analog of N-2-vinylpyrrolidone is being investigated
to compete with some of the existing markets for PVP. It is
believed that the mode of preparation of N-vinyl-2-oxazoli-
done by American Cyanamid involves the use of diethyl carbonate and diethanolamine, although ethylene carbonate
possibly will be used with subsequent savings in cost. A
recently issued patent to Cyanamid indicates that this material
may be used to plasticize various acrylonitrile compositions
(U.S. 2,786,043).

It is believed that PVP can be manufactured not in excess
of 75 cents per lb, which is considerably less expensive than
vinyl oxazolidone.

POLYVINYL ETHERS

A number of polyvinyl ethers are commercially produced.
Perhaps the best known alkyl vinyl ethers are methyl, ethyl,
n-butyl and isobutyl. These monomers readily polymerize in
the presence of Friedel-Crafts type catalysts. Polyvinyl methyl
ether (PVM) is a balsam-like polymer which is soluble in
cold water and in all organic solvents except naphtha. The
material is a sticky liquid which is light yellow to amber in
color and is obtained in a specific viscosity range (1 g in
100 ml of benzene at 25°C) of 0.5-0.9. The material is outstanding in the tack which it imparts to various formulations
of adhesives, cements, latexes and various coatings. A non-
migratory plasticizing action is contributed to a number of
water-soluble and organic-soluble resins. PVM is resistant
to leaching by water from these resins, and is not soluble
in hot water.

At room temperature PVM is extremely tacky, although
if the temperature is sufficiently lowered a brittle, non-tacky

solid results. General Aniline & Film Corporation reports that this "tack-free point" is only slightly affected by the degree of polymerization. The tack of the polymer is also unaffected by changes in humidity. Although the polymer does not contain a light stabilizer, it is relatively stable to ultraviolet radiation.

If PVM is stabilized against degradation at high temperature by a number of stabilizers (one of which is *p*-phenylphenol), prolonged heating at 100°C. for as long as one week does not result in degradation. PVM in 25% concentration is compatible in films with a number of materials. Among these polymers are natural rubber, neoprene, polystyrene, vinyl chloride-vinylidene chloride copolymer, vinyl chloride-vinyl acetate copolymer, polyvinyl acetate, chlorinated rubber, phenolic and alkyd resins, ethyl cellulose and cellulose nitrate.

PVM can tolerate limited amounts of inorganic salts without precipitation. The material also dissolves in glacial or dilute acetic acid without discoloration or degradation, but it is unstable in mineral acids. The polymer is insoluble and apparently stable in dilute and concentrated caustic.

Polyvinyl Isobutyl Ether

PVI is outstanding for its adhesiveness, electrical properties and plasticity. The material exhibits good solubility in a wide range of organic solvents. It is available from General Aniline & Film Corporation as 100% solids in three molecular weight grades. The high polymer is a white, opaque elastomer similar in appearance to crepe rubber while the medium molecular weight polymer is a very viscous, tacky liquid which is light orange to yellow in color. Low molecular weight polymer is less viscous and is an orange, tacky liquid. This polymer is soluble in hydrocarbons, chlorinated hydrocarbons, esters, ethers, higher alcohols and ketones. The properties of PVI are similar to those of polyvinyl methyl ether and will not be detailed.

Copolymers of Alkyl Vinyl Ethers

Lower alkyl vinyl ethers readily copolymerize with maleic anhydride and esters of fumaric acid and maleic acid. One of these copolymers, produced by General Aniline & Film, is a linear copolymer consisting of alternating methyl vinyl ether and maleic anhydride units. PVM/MA has infinite solubility in water, and is obtainable in a wide range of viscosities from high solids and low viscosity solutions to low solids and high viscosity solutions. The specific viscosity range measured in solutions of 1 g of the copolymer in 100 ml of methyl ethyl ketone at 25°C. is 0.2 to 3. The polymer is obtained as a white, amorphous powder of bulk density 16 lbs/cu ft and specific gravity of 1.3 to 1.4. PVM/MA is soluble in water and alcohols (dissolves with chemical reaction), acetone, methyl ethyl ketone, cyclohexanone, methyl acetate, benzaldehyde and pyridine. PVM/MA is insoluble in aliphatic and aromatic hydrocarbons and their halogen derivatives, ethyl ether and nitroparaffins. It is compatible with a wide variety of water soluble gums, resins and plasticizers.

The copolymer slowly absorbs moisture from the atmosphere. No marked changes in appearance or physical properties occur when the dry powder is heated for four weeks at 100°C. The half esters of the polymer are obtained when the polymer is dissolved in simple alcohols as well as methyl carbitol. It is found that a variation of viscosity of aqueous solutions is induced by increasing the pH by the addition of sodium hydroxide.

The maximum viscosity is obtained at a pH value of about 6, and this maximum is about ten times as great as the simple solution of the polymer. Alkalies cause no change in physical appearance of aqueous polymer in solution other than the viscosity effect. Similarly, sulfuric, hydrochloric, phosphoric and acetic acids show no effect on aqueous solutions of polymer when as much as 25% acid based on the polymer is added. Inorganic salts in large amounts are tolerated except in a few cases where insoluble gels or precipitates are formed. PVM/MA is compatible with a wide variety of water soluble gums and resins. Some of these materials are methyl cellulose, polyvinyl alcohol, phenol-formaldehyde resins and various protenoid materials.

PVM/MA is modified to a half amide, which is a water-soluble polymer. The nitrogen content of this material is 10.5-12.5%, which indicates that approximately ¾ of the anhydride groups have been converted. The polymer is believed to be semi-commercial by General Aniline & Film.

POLYVINYLCARBAZOLE

Carbazole and acetylene combine catalytically under high pressure to form N-vinylcarbazole, a vinyl amine. The monomer has a melting point of 61-65°C. and boils at 110°C. at 1 mm pressure. It is soluble in methyl and ethyl alcohol, pentane, cyclohexane, carbon tetrachloride, ethyl acetate and other solvents. The outstanding commercial application of the monomer is its use as a dielectric impregnant for stationary electrical assemblies.

The polymer is a gray to light brown thermoplastic which is commercially available in a form varying from powder to broken lumps. The outstanding characteristics of the polymer are its excellent electrical properties which are retained even at elevated temperatures and over a broad frequency range, and its high heat distortion point; the latter having an ASTM value of 140 to 160°C. The polymer is resistant to mineral oils, carbon tetrachloride, ether, alcohol, water, dilute alkalies and acids, and hydrogen fluoride, as well as aliphatic and aromatic hydrocarbons in general.

VINYL CHLORIDE POLYMERS

The most important members of the vinyl family from the standpoint of volume and economic position are vinyl chloride and its copolymers. Well over 100 commercial vinyl chloride resins are known, and it is not feasible to enumerate any of them specifically. In general, one need only state that suspension resins are the most important in this country and dispersion (emulsion) resins follow in volume. Suspension and dispersion resins do not compete with one another in that for the most part their markets are divergent.

Dry Blending

The relatively new technique of "dry-blending" can be described as the technique of compounding resins, plasticizers, stabilizers, lubricants, fillers and colors in the form of a dry, free-flowing powder. This technique has mildly revolutionized this industry.

The nature of the resin particle is a primary factor in determining the characteristics of a good dry-blending resin. PVC prepared by the emulsion process does not dry-blend. Resin formed by suspension can be made capable of dry-blending by certain polymerization formulations. A good dry-blending PVC is a porous particle which can absorb a large volume of plasticizer and exhibit a minimum wetness. It is believed by some that the most desirable particle for this application is one which is more spherical than irregular in shape, although this is in dispute by others. Those resins which exhibit the most uniformity of particle size have the greatest consistency of dry-blending. This is obvious since particles of approximately the same size and shape compete for plasticizer with relatively the same order of magnitude. Some processors of PVC who use the dry-blending technique will first charge the resin to a ribbon-type or other blender which is pre-heated to 150°F. or higher. The plasticizer is heated and sprayed over the resin. This plasticizer may be a single material such as DOP or a mixture of monomeric plasticizers containing some polymeric plasticizer. A usual ratio of resin to plasticizer is 100 to 50 for flexible materials, although the amount of plasticizer may be in excess of this figure. The ratio is varied depending upon the type of processing to be used, for example, extrusion, molding, calendering and the properties desired. In addition to the plasticizer various other materials such as stabilizers, colors, fillers and certain specialty lubricants are often added. Many different plasticizers or plasticizer combinations are employed.

The newer dry-blending resins are of interest to processors due to the ease of either hot- or cold-blending, high degree of plasticizer absorption resulting in a uniform dry-blend, free-flowing hot pre-mixes, rapid fusion on mill, calender, or internal mixers, good heat stability, high throughput rate in processing equipment, low gel count, excellent color and clarity and high surface luster.

It is certainly conceivable that within a few years these easy-processing resins will almost completely replace the older suspension PVC. On the other hand, dispersion resins for organosol and plastisol applications are increasing in volume. The field of paste resin use is certainly capable of large strides in the next decade.

The average molecular weight of PVC determines its use and applications. Higher molecular weight resins find major applications in extrusions of flexible tubing, welting, the electrical industry, garden hose and calendered film. Intermediate and lower molecular weight resins are used in film and sheeting, coated fabrics and in rigid applications. A resin of relative viscosity of about 1.75 (1% in cyclohexanone at 25°C.) is believed to be the minimum viscosity obtainable in useful form without modification. Values lower than this are obtained by copolymerizing vinyl chloride with various minor amounts of other ingredients or by other modifications.

The properties of PVC and a number of copolymers of vinyl chloride are so affected by polymerization conditions, plasticizers (if used and of what type) and the manner that the compounded material is fabricated, it is difficult to pinpoint a resin for specific applications based solely on molecular weight. PVC and its important vinyl chloride-acetate copolymer are used for the manufacture of flexible film and sheeting, rigid and elastomeric extrusion compounds, laminated film, rigid sheets, molding compounds, monofilaments, floor coverings, coated fabrics and paper, and surface coatings. These will be discussed under applications.

A number of different methods of reporting viscosity as a function of average molecular weight are used. A good method is the determination of relative viscosity in a 1% solution of polymer in cyclohexanone at 25°C. Cyclohexanone is a desirable solvent and good reproducibility is obtained. The highest molecular weight unmodified PVC may require gentle heating in order to effect solution.

The relative viscosity of PVC by this method is a maximum value of about 2.6, while completely unmodified material has a minimum viscosity of approximately 1.75. Polymers which exhibit molecular weight in excess of this uppermost viscosity figure of 2.6 are generally too difficult to process using conventional machinery and equipment. Unmodified PVC of a relative viscosity much below 1.75 is generally very poor in heat stability and often shows pinkish color in the appearance of the bulk resin.

The volatile content of PVC after drying in the factory should not be in excess of 0.5% for most molecular weight grades. It is found, however, that some lower molecular weight materials contain approximately 0.75% of volatile matter; this volatile matter being essentially water, but sometimes comprising vinyl chloride monomer.

The bulk density of PVC varies widely as some of the newer lower molecular weight materials have a value of approximately 45 lbs/cu ft, while other homopolymers are as low as 20 lbs/cu ft, or lower. However, high bulk density in most applications does permit a greater throughput using certain processing equipment. A broad general statement can be made that lower bulk density polymers absorb greater amounts of plasticizer and still permit free-flowing of the dry-blended material. The general properties of suspension PVC powder are in Table 2.14. It is usually desirable to manufacture a coarser PVC if the gel or "fisheye" is not increased. Most manufacturers attempt to prepare suspension polymer all of which will pass a 40 mesh U. S. standard sieve and little if any pass a 200 mesh sieve.

TABLE 2.14. GENERAL POWDER PROPERTIES OF SUSPENSION PVC

Specific gravity	1.40
Bulk density, lb/ft.[3]	16-45
Relative viscosity, 1% in cyclohexanone @ 25°C.	1.75-2.60

Screen analysis:

% Retained on 80 mesh	0-100
% Through 200 mesh	0-100
Heat loss, % at 105°C.	0-0.75
Color	White to pinkish
Heat stability (plasticized and stabilized)	Fair—excellent
Light stability (plasticized and stabilized)	Good
Toxicity, odor, taste	None
Flammability	Self-extinguishing

Chemical resistance:

Alcohols	Resists aliphatics
Aldehydes	Resists formaldehyde
Alkalies	Excellent
Acids (inorganic)	Resists most
Acids (organic)	Resists most except acetic
Esters	Soften
Vegetable oils	Excellent
Water	Excellent
Halogenated hydrocarbons, ketones, phenols	Poor

Great variations are observed in resins some of which have zero to total retention on 80 and 100 mesh screens, while other PVC will show 30-40% or more as "fines" which pass a 200 mesh screen. These latter polymers are dusty and offer handling and processing difficulties not characteristic of coarser polymer. The dust problem can become severe, particularly when bags of the polymer are emptied into the various processing equipment. Some fabricators prefer to convey polymer by air conveying ducts, and dusty polymer is particularly difficult to handle in such a manner.

"Fisheyes" are of great interest to most compounders of polyvinyl chloride in the form of film, sheeting and extrusions, as well as certain critical molding applications. Fisheyes are gelatinous particles which do not readily absorb plasticizer and thus appear as discrete gel particles in the finished material. This is described in detail in Chapter 4.

Dispersion Resins

A limited number of dispersion resins are prominent in the United States. Among these materials are "Exon" 654 (Firestone), "Bakelite" QYNV, "Marvinol" VR-50 and VR-51 (Naugatuck), "Geon" 121 (Goodrich) and "Opalon" 410 (Monsanto). These materials have an ASTM specific viscosity in the general range of 0.50 and particle size of about 1.5 microns. The bulk density of all these materials is relatively low when compared to most suspension resins, varying from approximately 16 to 21 lb/cu ft. It is well known that dispersion resins are considerably poorer in heat stability than suspension resins.

The majority of dispersion grade resins are stirred into the plasticizer and for this reason are sometimes spoken of as "stir-in" resins. A proper particle size distribution is of critical importance in the performance of stir-in resins, and if a wide variation in micron size is present operational difficulties invariably result. In addition to the particle size distribution other physical properties such as shape and density of the particles as well as their molecular weight become factors. If the particle size is especially large in emulsion resins, it may become necessary to grind in order to obtain a proper dispersion. These dispersion resins are therefore known as "grind-in" resins.

In virtually all plastic applications the lower the molecular weight of the resin, the lower the processing temperature required. It is particularly true that low molecular weights are generally desirable in dispersion resins, but this must not be at the expense of lowering the viscosity stability of the material. It is essential in the manufacture of low viscosity dispersion resins for plastisol and organosol applications that the resin does not absorb plasticizer and thus become solvated. The basic character of the resin itself provides desirable low initial viscosity, but this can be supplemented by external means, such as the amount and type of plasticizer employed, as well as the incorporation of any of a number of non-ionic surface active agents. In those rare cases in which low initial viscosity is objectionable, certain metallic soaps which are often used as stabilizers do increase this initial viscosity. When the particle size is extremely small poor viscosity stability results due to solvation in the plasticizer.

A high concentration of emulsifier in the latex is important because the polymer sphericals are coated and thus are made resistant to attack of the plasticizer. Perhaps of lesser importance is the fact that a hard, relatively impervious particle also resists solvation.

Dispersion resins, when applied as a paste in plasticizer, are known as "plastisols"; when applied with small amounts of volatile organic liquids they are called "organosols."

Dispersion resins are used in all vinyl foams. Vinyl foams can be prepared either of an open cell or closed cell types. Cellular PVC has good flame resistance in either cell type. A wide range of densities are possible, from minimums of 2-3 lb/cu ft for closed cell and from 4-5 lb for open cell. The resistance of cellular PVC to various chemicals is similar to that of plasticized PVC film and sheeting. The foamed product is also resistant to ozone, oxygen, oils, moisture and sea water. The resistance to sunlight opens new channels for applications of the thermoplastic material. Foam PVC has good load-bearing capacity and a wide range of resiliencies is possible. Properly fused open cell foam has a low permanent set. This is of importance in upholstery applications, as it allows cushion material to recover quickly its original shape and appearance. Flame resistance is of particular importance in seating used in public transportation and in cushioning for crash pads in aircraft.

The total consumption (sale) of all dispersion resins in this country in 1957 is believed not to be in excess of 75 million lb. The price is 30 cents per pound.

Low Molecular Weight Resin

There is an increasing tendency to use lower molecular weight suspension polymer in this country. In the past it has been true that lower molecular weight polymer had markedly less heat resistance than its higher molecular weight counterparts. A few resins manufactured show little degradation in heat stability between high, intermediate and lower molecular weight PVC. As quite low molecular weight materials—in the vicinity of 1.85 relative viscosity—can be prepared without modification, excellent heat stability is obtained.

The use of lower molecular weight polymer permits more rapid throughput of certain processing equipment. For example, it is found when processing polymer that low average molecular weight resin permits extremely rapid fusion. For many applications there is not enough difference in heat distortion temperature between high and relatively low molecular weights to warrant use of the former, as lower processing temperatures are preferable. A marked case in point involves the present trend of utilization of low molecular weight polymer in rigid applications.

Two types of rigid PVC are common. Type I is unmodified or essentially unmodified PVC, processed with a minimum amount of additives. In the simplest form this may consist of two to three parts of a stabilizer with possibly the inclusion of a lesser amount of a lubricant. These materials exhibit high heat distortion temperatures and minimum impact strength, the latter not being in excess of 1 ft-lb/in of notch (Izod).

Type II rigids utilize N-type rubbers in concentrations of from 5-20% or more based on the PVC. These rubbers in conjunction with stabilizers, fillers, and possibly other additives permit maximum impact strength, which in certain cases produce Izod values of 20 ft-lb/in of notch, or more. The use of rubber smoothes out the processing of the vinyl and permits excellent fabrication without surface defects and thus presents greater application. Type I vinyls has greater chemical resistance than Type II, although the latter is generally good.

Rigid PVC has excellent corrosion resistance, particularly Type I product. Exceptional corrosion resistance in both 80% sulfuric acid and 50% sodium hydroxide is obtained when comparison is made to stainless steel. In oil field piping Type I rigids have one outstanding advantage over polyethylene; this is the failure of paraffinic products to deposit on the interior of the walls of PVC pipe and thus restrict the volume of flow. This is particularly objectionable in the case of polyethylene. Soil burial tests of PVC under acidic conditions indicate longer service life for this vinyl over various conventional metal pipes. An outstanding difference between Types I and II is the markedly improved chemical resistance of Type I in 80% sulfuric acid, 60% nitric acid and 50% hydrogen peroxide. After prolonged exposure of Type I PVC to the above chemicals, tensile strength, flex, impact strength and heat distortion remain high. Outdoor aging of Type I and Type II vinyls is excellent.

(Courtesy Seiberling Plastics Company)

Figure 2.3. Rigid vinyl laminate.

High-impact vinyl pipe has been extensively installed on U.S. Navy warships for conveying sea water for wash-down purposes of the entire ship's exterior in case of atomic attack. The excellent corrosion resistance and light weight led to the selection of PVC as the standard material of construction. A military specification MIL-P-19119 (ships) has been issued which states a short time hydrostatic burst pressure of 1,000 psi minimum at room temperature and 500 psi at 145°F. must be met. Hydrostatic burst specifications is 900 psi minimum after 500 psi exposure for 24 hr and 900 psi minimum after a pressure cycling test of 6 cycles per hr between 0 and 500 psi for 7 hr. Impact qualifications require the material to survive impact of a 4-in. diameter steel ball of 9.3 lb dropped from a height of 10 ft for a varying number of blows depending upon the size of the pipe. The relatively low cost, ease of assembly and non-flammability all favor the acceptance of PVC pipe.

Solvent cementing of rigid vinyl pipe is having increased application as well as joining by threaded fittings and a hot gas welding technique.

Both Type I and Type II rigids are used in pipe, skylights, valves, tank linings and flume ducts. The high impact strengths, chemical resistance, relatively high heat distortion temperatures, non-flammability and non-toxic nature contribute to increased importance of these and other rigid products.

Table 2.15 lists the general properties of flexible and rigid PVC.

Rigid sheets and pipe extrusions most often are processed from intermediate and preferably lower molecular weight material. Rigid sheet is often made from unplasticized vinyl chloride-vinyl acetate copolymer. This material is supplied in continuous rolls and has a grained surface finish. In thicknesses of .01 in. and up, sheets are surfaced-finished with a high gloss applied by press polishing; or a matte finish is applied to both sides, or one side press-polished and the other matte-finished. The copolymer sheeting can be used at temperatures up to 60°C. It is found that rigid sheet has exceptional dimensional stability in that it contains no volatile plasticizers and will not warp under normal conditions of aging.

The general physical characteristics, uniform thermal plasticity, and homogeneity of vinyl chloride-vinyl acetate rigid sheet after heating permit remarkable extensibility, which is necessary in deep drawing. Rigid sheet is finding many industrial applications which require resistance to strong alkalies, inorganic acids (including hydrofluoric acid), and other ma-

TABLE 2.15. PROPERTIES OF FLEXIBLE AND RIGID PVC

	Flexible PVC	Rigid PVC (Unmodified)
Specific gravity	1.20-1.55	1.32-1.40
Ultimate tensile strength, psi, max.	3,500	9,000
Ultimate tensile strength, psi, ave.	1,500-3,500	5,500-8,000
Flexural strength, psi.	8,000-16,000	14,000
Ultimate elongation, %	200-450	5-25
Modulus elasticity in tension, psi	—	350,000-400,000
Hardness, shore durometer	50-100A	70-85D
Hardness, Rockwell R Scale	—	120
Compressive strength, psi	—	10,000-13,000
Max. service temp., °F.	170-220	150
Izod impact strength, notched, ft-lb/in.	—	1 max.
Minimum flex temp., °F.	0 to −70	—
Electrical properties		
Volume resistivity, ohm-cm 25°C., max.	$1\text{-}10 \times 10^{12}$ to $4\text{-}7 \times 10^{14}$	$1\text{-}5 \times 10^{14}$ to $1\text{-}5 \times 10^{16}$
Dielectric constant at 60 cycles at 25°C.	5.5-9.0	2.3-3.7
Dielectric strength, volts/mil— 30 mil specimen	—	800
Power factor at 60 cycles at 25°C.	0.05-0.15	0.02-0.03
Thermal properties		
Thermal conductivity, 10^4 cal/sec/cm²/°C./cm	3-4	3.7
Thermal expansion, 10^5/°C.	—	5-7
Heat Distortion Temp, °F. @ 264 psi	—	140-170
Specific heat, cal/°C./g	0.2-0.28	0.3-0.5

terials. Rigid vinyls are also unaffected by gasoline, kerosene, aliphatic alcohols, aliphatic hydrocarbons, and animal, mineral and vegetable oils. These properties indicate that in a few years increased use of unplasticized vinyl film in food wrappings and containers will result.

Copolymers of vinyl chloride and vinyl acetate possess excellent dimentional stability and resistance to warpage over extreme temperature and humidity conditions. The ability to mold this material to extremely close tolerances coupled with exceptionally low mold shrinkage allow near perfect reproduction of the mold surface. For these reasons vinyls have replaced shellac for phonograph records, and the fidelity of vinyl chloride-vinyl acetate copolymers is also better than polystyrene. The records may be dropped or bent without shattering and characteristically have a minimum of surface noise.

Floor coverings are made of both vinyl chloride-acetate copolymer and PVC. The ease of cleaning and beauty of these coverings has led to their widespread popularity, and the highly resistant nature of the composition toward staining from foods, oils or greases and other spillage is recognized. The wear-resistant properties of the floor coverings, the wide range of color possibilities and the marked resistance of the flooring to light, aging and household detergents all contribute to its popularity.

Vinyl chloride-acetate resin coatings are well regarded by the industry in protecting various surfaces. Air-dry or baked finishes are tough, have excellent gloss, adhesion and chemical resistance on metals, paper, concrete, cloth, and wall tile. The absence of odor, taste, and toxicity combined with good water resistance and chemical inertness, excellent toughness and flexibility, good clarity, nonflammability and resistance to age and weathering all lead to the popularity of these copolymer coatings.

Suspension resin is of great importance in the electrical

industry. The ease of washing to remove various impurities which may be present in suspension systems offers a marked advantage over the emulsion system for the preparation of electrical grade resin. The highly important electrical wire and cable usage is continuing to grow at a rapid rate. High molecular weight, easy-processing resins are used in greatest quantity by the electrical industry. Wire coatings which must carry more than 600 volts or be subject for service in wet locations cannot be used.

Flexible film is often made from higher molecular weight polymer. The greater heat history in processing film over sheeting permits the use of high molecular weight resin, and this higher heat history helps eliminate gel particles. Supported and unsupported sheeting are most often processed from intermediate molecular weight polymer. The newer extruded and blown PVC in this country is produced from high and intermediate molecular weight resins.

European efforts toward after-chlorinating of PVC have not found favor in this country. The objective in such a procedure is to increase solubility of the polymer, but this is attended by very poor heat and light stability, low softening temperatures and brittleness.

Stabilization

In most applications it is essential that the vinyls be well stabilized against thermal degradation of processing. Certain requirements of non-toxicity do not permit the use of normal heavy metal stabilizers, but in these few applications non-toxic stabilizers are employed. Without the use of stabilizers vinyl chloride polymers dehydrochlorinate with rapid failure of mechanical properties after this degradation reaches an advanced state. It is important to the processor of vinyls to realize that heat stability tests of uncompounded and unstabilized vinyl chloride polymer and copolymers are unreliable. Some manufacturers incorporate various metallic salts and other additives in the polymerization formulation and some of these additives impart some degree of heat stabilization. Although the amount and type of these ingredients do not change the normal heat history of processing in properly stabilized formulations, incipient stabilization is imparted to the resin powder. In order that a heat stabilization test be meaningful it is therefore necessary to conduct laboratory heat stability studies on fully compounded formulations.

High molecular weight polymer generally produces compounded products of the greatest clarity and best color. Lower molecular weight PVC prepared at higher temperatures of polymerization, or by copolymerization of vinyl chloride with other monomers are generally somewhat poorer in color and clarity. Despite the fact that high molecular weight polymer has excellent color and clarity, it is necessary to stabilize this molecular weight grade at approximately the same concentration of stabilizers as with lower molecular weight resin. The higher processing temperatures required for high molecular weight resins necessitate ample stabilization because of the added heat history involved.

The most important class of stabilizers are metallo-organic compounds. In addition to these more widely used stabilizers, to a much lesser extent various weakly alkaline compounds find service because of their ability to combine with hydrogen chloride which is evolved as a product of decomposition. The stabilizers are prepared by a number of United States manufacturers which include Argus Chemical, Metal & Thermit, National Lead, Advance Solvents, Metasap, Nuodex Products, Harshaw Chemical, Ferro Chemical, and Witco Chemical.

Most of the stabilizers used are liquids which are often metallic salts of fatty acids or soaps. If these stabilizers are in solid form they can be most effectively added by mixing with fillers which permit better dispersion of the stabilizer.

The number of stabilizing ingredients which have been added to vinyl chloride polymers is so great that they will not be enumerated except in a general manner. The basic stabilizers are many alkali or alkaline earth oxides as well as organic products including amines. A highly important group of stabilizers comprises the alkyl and aryl metallic compounds. Sulfur-containing tin compounds find considerable application in rigid applications. In addition to the metal soaps and esters of tin compounds barium and cadmium compounds are becoming increasingly important. Lead compounds still are widely used, although care must be exercised to avoid cross-staining by contamination with sulfur-containing compounds. Lead compounds find large application in electrical compounding. The quantity of heat stabilizers used greatly depends upon the specific application. Concentrations of 2 to 3 parts of heat stabilizer or more are often employed.

Light stabilizers must be used for certain outdoor applications, and in these the concentration of light stabilizer additive is in the category of several percent. Among the older light stabilizers are salicylates, and in particular phenyl salicylate, although benzoates are also used. Recently an effective material for the absorption of radiation in the ultraviolet portion of the spectrum is 2-hydroxy-4-methoxybenzophenone. This particular material does not fluoresce but emits the light energy it absorbs as harmless radiation.

Certain resin polymerization systems, because of their inherent nature, require higher levels of stabilizers to give the same performance characteristics as those obtained by other polymerization formulations. It is found that certain suspending agents used in resin preparation do not give resin stability of other suspending materials. The choice and concentration of catalyst used in polymerization affects resin stability, resins of lower stability being obtained with higher catalyst concentrations and higher reaction temperatures. The purity of the monomer is also of importance in contributing to the stability of the polymer prepared from it.

A number of different buffers are added by various manufacturers in emulsion and suspension polymerization. These materials are used because of their generally desirable effect upon the polymerization system, and also because a certain initial stability is imparted to the finished polymer.

The full effect of the presence of lower molecular weight polymer in any vinyl polymerization is not completely understood. It is true that excessive quantities of low molecular weight fragments in a given polymer do give poorer stability than those polymers of the same average molecular weight but which are composed of smaller quantities of lower molecular weight polymer.

Plasticizers

In all non-rigid applications regardless of type plasticizers are employed. The most widely used plasticizers are esters and in particular dioctylphthalate, both di-2-ethylhexyl and di-*n*-octylphthalate, the former in greater volume.

Various adipates and sebacates also are used for specialty applications involving low-temperature service. Phosphate esters have importance particularly in flame-proofing compounds. Epoxy compounds, such as epoxidized soybean oil, are gaining increasing popularity as non-fugitive plasticizers, although many materials of this type must be used as secondary plasticizers due to their relatively low compatibility with PVC. A number of cheap hydrocarbon extenders are useful in combination with primary plasticizers only. Increased emphasis in research laboratories has been placed upon attempted preparation of "non-plasticizing plasticizers." These materials are desired to allow processing of the vinyls under conditions approaching those of normal ester-type plasticizers and which later upon the application of heat become rigid and no longer impart a plasticizing action. Some limited success has been achieved in this direction through the use of alkyl glycol methacrylates. DOP is still the "universal" plasticizer and is

Vinyl Resins

approved for non-toxic applications. This plasticizer when distilled gives the maximum in color and clarity of processed resin.

VINYLIDENE CHLORIDE POLYMERS

The first vinylidene chloride polymers were commercially introduced by Dow in 1940. Vinylidene chloride is a clear, colorless liquid having a boiling point of 31.7°C. The homopolymer is of limited commercial importance due to its essen-

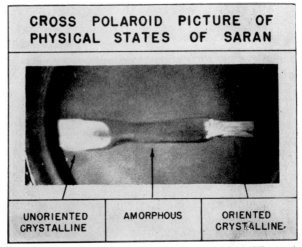

CROSS POLAROID PICTURE OF PHYSICAL STATES OF SARAN

| UNORIENTED CRYSTALLINE | AMORPHOUS | ORIENTED CRYSTALLINE |

(*Courtesy Dow Chemical Company*)

Figure 2.4.

tially infusable and intractable nature. Well stabilized systems do not soften until a temperature of about 200°C. is reached. These high temperatures are beyond the reach of normal processing equipment and also are close to decomposition temperature. The molecular weight of polyvinylidene chloride is a maximum of approximately 100,000. The copolymer of vinylidene chloride with vinyl chloride (85/15) has been developed by Dow as saran. A similar material is fabricated by Firestone as "Velon," while a higher percentage of vinyl chloride which permits greater shrinkage is marketed as film by Dewey & Almy as "Cryovac."

Copolymers of vinylidene chloride can be formed which have softening temperatures ranging from about 70°C. to 180°C. or higher. These vary in properties from soft, flexible materials to rigid products. Commercial products have a maximum softening temperature of about 140°C. and a molecular weight of about 20,000. Saran has regions of crystalline structure as demonstrated by its x-ray diffraction pattern, although most thermoplastics exist in an amorphous state and do not show such crystallinity. This crystalline structure is lost when the polymer is heated to fusion but is slowly regained upon cooling to room temperature. The general properties of a saran formulation are in Table 2.16. An outstanding characteristic of saran is its solvent and chemical resistance, which is particularly pronounced at room temperature when the polymer is in contact with all acids and all common alkalies except concentrated ammonium hydroxide. Saran is little affected by both aliphatic and aromatic hydrocarbons, esters, ketones, alcohols and nitroparaffins. Swelling does occur in cyclohexanone and dioxane. This material exhibits extremely low water absorption and vapor transmission; water absorption over 24 hr by the ASTM method is 0-.05%.

It is significant that the chemical resistance of this polymer is partly a function of crystallinity, as the crystalline form has higher chemical resistance than the amorphous form. The polymer is non-flammable, odorless, tasteless and non-toxic, while toughness and abrasion resistance are high which contribute to long wearing qualities. The maximum service temperature of finished saran is 250°F. This polymer is adapted to extrusion, calendering and molding applications. A softening temperature of 240-280°F. is applicable for injection,

TABLE 2.16. GENERAL PROPERTIES OF A SARAN FORMULATION

Effect of weak acids	None
Effect of strong acids	Darkens in H_2SO_4—others none
Effect of weak alkalies	None
Effect of strong alkalies	Affected by NH_4OH, darkens in caustic, others none
Effect of organic solvents	Highly resistant
Water absorption ASTM D570-40T	Less than 0.1%
Water permeability	Very low
Burning rate	Self extinguishing
Thermal conductivity	2.2×10^{-4} cal/sec/sq cm/°C./cm
Specific heat	.316 cal/°C./gm
Index of refraction	1.61
Specific gravity	1.70
Volume resistivity D.C.	10^{14}-10^{16} ohm cms
Dielectric strength 60 cycles	500-3000 volts/mil
Dielectric constant 60 cycles	4
Power factor 60 cycles	.03-.08
Effect of age	None
Effect of sunlight	Slight
Machinability	Good
Color possibilities	Extensive

compression or transfer molding. Extrudable formulations can be obtained using 5 parts of a plasticizer, and 2 parts each of a heat stabilizer and light stabilizer to 100 parts of resin. α-Methylbenzyl ether is a good plasticizer and salol a good light stabilizer. Heat stabilizers used are generally those which are not conventional to the stabilization of vinyl chloride polymers. The tendency of exudation of plasticizers is marked when saran-type polymers contain more than 5% plasticizer by weight and the polymer is oriented. This orientation markedly increases exudation tendencies of the plasticizer. The latest price quotation for Saran B-115 in 20,000 lb quantities is 39 cents per lb.

Polystyrene quite properly belongs in any presentation of

the vinyl family. However, styrene (vinyl benzene) will not be discussed here.

European Developments

In general, the development of PVC in western Europe is somewhat behind that in the United States. Certain technical developments have been made in Europe of varying degrees of success. The Europeans are generally converting from the emulsion process to the more widely used (in the United States) process of suspension polymerization.

At least two types of copolymers are made in Germany which are not manufactured in the United States. One of these is a copolymer of vinyl chloride and styrene and has applications in floor covering. A product called "Gepolit" is made by an emulsion process by Chemische Werke Huls. A second interesting copolymer comprising 40% vinyl acetate and 60% vinyl chloride is made by a suspension method and is used in lacquers. This product is manufactured by Wacker Chemie.

The greater use of PVC in rigid applications in Europe results in emphasis of the European research and development effort along such lines. The popular technique of dry blending in the United States is little used in European countries.

3. CHEMISTRY

POLYVINYL CHLORIDE

The most important polymer in the vinyl family is poly-vinyl chloride. This polymer is made from vinyl chloride monomer, a relatively non-toxic, sweet-smelling and flammable material. The monomer boils at $-14°C$., and freezes at $-160°C$. Its density at 20°C. is 0.91 and index of refraction at 15° is 1.38. In the production of polymers of vinyl chloride great care must be taken so that explosions and fires do not result. Vinyl chloride monomer has flammable limits of 4-22% by volume in air. The heat of polymerization is approximately 23 Kcal per mole.

Monomer Preparation

One of the methods of preparation of vinyl chloride monomer is by the addition of 1.38 lb hydrochloric acid to 1 lb of acetylene in either a liquid or a gaseous state. The liquid process requires the acetylene to be conducted into a mixed solution of concentrated hydrochloric acid and cupric chloride catalyst at approximately 20°C. The resulting vinyl chloride is fractionally separated from the mixture. In the so-called "dry" process, a dry acetylene-hydrochloric acid mixture containing an excess of catalyst is passed over a number of plates which contain the catalyst. One of the more popular catalysts is mercuric chloride impregnated on acti-

(*Courtesy Escambia Chemical Corporation*)

Figure 3.1. Experimental reactor for vinyl monomers.

vated charcoal pellets. The reaction is carried out at temperatures as high as 200°C. It is reported that a conversion of 10% produces yields up to 95%. After the condensation of vinyl chloride and higher-boiling materials, the liquid reaction products are fractionated, the vinyl chloride removed at the top of the column, and the high-boiling materials collected in the still pot. In the manufacture of vinyl chloride from ethylene, 2.4 lb of chlorine are required per lb of ethylene. By-product hydrogen chloride is 1.16 lb and monomer 1.89 lb.

Catalytic pyrolysis of dichloroethane also produces vinyl chloride. This temperature may be as high as 1000°C. though various activated catalysts permit substantially lower temperatures of operation.

Regardless of the method used to prepare vinyl chloride monomer, the product must be of maximum possible purity and contain low concentrations of aldehydes, iron, acetylenes and acidity. Phenol is added as a polymerization inhibitor.

Kinetic studies of vinyl polymerizations have indicated that this polymerization is initiated by the formation of free-radical monomer molecules, each of these having a free electron. Initiators can be provided by heat, light, or chemical materials to form high polymeric substances. Initiators in vinyl polymerization can be of either a water-soluble or an oil-soluble type. Potassium and ammonium persulfate and hydrogen peroxide are water-soluble, while lauroyl and benzoyl peroxide are examples of free radical-initiating materials of oil-soluble type. Generally the less catalyst used, the higher the molecular weight of the polymer. Many redox systems have been studied in which initiation generates free radicals by oxidation-reduction reaction at relatively low temperatures. Redox systems sometimes employed consist of potassium persulfate-sodium bisulfite, and hydrogen peroxide-ferrous sulfate. Rapid polymerization rates are obtained by redox catalysts.

Polymerization

Vinyl chloride polymerizes slowly in the dark and more rapidly in the presence of light. This was established by Regnault in 1838. In 1914 it was shown that this slow polymerization of vinyl chloride is markedly accelerated by the addition of certain catalysts, namely, benzoyl peroxide. Staudinger in 1930 studied the polymerization of vinyl chloride catalyzed by ultraviolet light. The polymer formed was not soluble in the monomer and was separated as a mixture of high and low polymers. Staudinger found that the average chain length was of the order of 50 monomer units, or an average molecular weight of about 3,000. The lower molecular weight members of this mixture can be extracted by benzene or carbon bisulfide. When the degree of polymerization of vinyl chloride is approximately 100, the polymer is no longer soluble in simple solvents. A generally accepted structure of polyvinyl chloride is as follows:

$$-CH_2-CH-CH_2-CH-CH_2-$$
$$\quad\quad\quad | \quad\quad\quad\quad |$$
$$\quad\quad\quad Cl \quad\quad\quad Cl$$

Later work of Staudinger in 1939 indicated that polyvinyl chloride obtained from different manufacturing sources of comparable molecular weight exhibit the same solution viscosities. This leads to the simple conclusion that the chains are unbranched. This concept is based on the fact that polymer materials with different degrees of branching but of the same molecular weight would exhibit different solution viscosities. The molecular weights of most commercial polyvinyl chloride are believed to lie between 50,000 and 150,000 as determined by osmotic pressure measurements. Such high polymers are characterized by a marked degree of solvent resistance and general resistance to chemical attack. Fractionation studies of commercial PVC indicate wide molecular weight distributions by many manufacturers. Such variations can offer difficulties to processors of the resin.

Vinyl chloride copolymerizes with a number of monomers, although not all vinyl compounds are copolymerizable. Different monomers enter the polymer structure at different reaction velocities. The chemical properties of the vinyls depend upon a number of factors. For example, very low polymers generally are considerably more soluble than those of a higher degree of polymerization. Crystalline high polymers such as polyvinylidene chloride are markedly insoluble;

this is due to some extent to the degree of polymerization. Structural dissimilarity in copolymers prohibits crystallization.

Certain other irregularities are discerned in vinyl copolymerizations. Both vinyl chloride and vinylidene chloride are inhibited in polymerization by the presence of the other. The copolymer thus polymerizes at a rate approximately $\frac{1}{10}$ that of either monomer. Physical and mechanical properties of both homo- and copolymers are also markedly affected by the degree of polymerization and the nature of the monomeric substances. Elastomeric properties depend upon the possibility of cross-linking. The non-cross-linked nature of vinyl chloride polymer does not permit elastomeric applications, in fact, it is found that zinc enables halogen to be removed from polyvinyl chloride molecules without cross-linking resulting.

The work of Professor Natta in Italy in the field of stereospecific polymerization of ethylene and propylene has not entirely neglected vinyl chloride polymers. The vinyls normally polymerize to yield products in which every other carbon atom is asymmetric. When conventional catalysts are used, a random distribution of *d* and *l* configurations around the carbon atoms are produced. This type of polymer Natta speaks of as being "atactic." "Isotactic" polymers are produced in which all the asymmetric carbon atoms are in the *d* or *l* configuration; these have varying degrees of crystallinity in the cases of the polymerization of ethylene and propylene. "Syndiotactic" polymers result in which polymerization produces a regular alteration of *d* and *l* configurations.

Attempts to produce an isotactic polymer of vinyl chloride have resulted in dehydrohalogenation. The resulting polymer is reputed to have only about 50% of the theoretical chlorine. It is possible that other catalysts or techniques will be developed which will enable the polymerization of vinyl chloride to proceed without such dehydrohalogenation. If isotactic PVC is obtained in the future, the commercial utilization will still be uncertain due to the higher softening temperatures of the resin requiring higher processing temperatures than some conventional equipment can deliver.

POLYVINYL ACETATE

The liquid or gaseous state reaction of acetic acid with acetylene is the commercial method of preparation of vinyl acetate. Mercuric sulfate as a catalyst used in conjunction with hot, dilute sulfuric acid readily hydrates acetylene to formation of acetaldehyde. The intermediate in this reaction is the unstable vinyl alcohol which readily isomerizes to the aldehyde.

The replacement of the mobile hydrogen by alkyl groups or acid residues produces derivatives of vinyl alcohol. The mercuric salt of acetylsulfuric acid is an excellent catalyst to use with acetic acid and acetylene in production of vinyl acetate. Perhaps mercuric sulfate is the best catalyst. This is prepared by dissolving mercuric oxide in glacial acetic acid and precipitating the sulfate by fuming sulfuric acid. Liquid phase reactions involve introducing acetylene into a mixed solution of glacial acetic acid containing the catalyst at temperatures generally in the range of 75°C. Vinyl acetate is removed by dilution in excess acetylene, and then fractionally distilled to produce the pure monomer of boiling point 73°C. Vapor phase formation is conducted at temperatures in excess of 200°C. using metal catalysts impregnated on absorbers such as activated charcoal or activated alumina.

Vinyl acetate under the influence of a peroxide such as benzoyl peroxide and heat gives polyvinyl acetate. The structure of the polymer is:

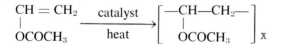

After the initiation under the influence of the catalyst, the free radicals rapidly add to monomer molecules in a propagation step. The propagation or polymerization is continued until reaction is terminated by combination with another free radical or by a chain-transfer mechanism.

It is significant that the entire process involving the polymerization of a single polymer chain is very rapid and constitutes only a small time portion of the over-all conversion, as the polymer chain usually does not further increase in length during latter stages of polymerization.

POLYVINYL ALCOHOL

Hydrolysis of polyvinyl acetate produces polyvinyl alcohol:

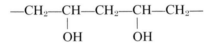

Polyvinyl acetals are prepared by condensation of the hydroxyl groups in polyvinyl alcohol with various aldehydes.

While PVC is a stable molecule, polyvinyl alcohol readily undergoes a number of chemical reactions quite similar to those of lower aliphatic alcohols. Some of the more interesting reactions involve the reaction of PVA with boric acid to form polyvinyl borate, an inorganic ester. Organic esters such as polyvinyl sulfonate result from reaction with alkyl or aryl sulfonates. Shawinigan states that reaction of PVA with cinnamoyl chloride forms the ester of the unsaturated acid, which is a solvent-soluble, film-forming, light-sensitive material. An even more light-sensitive polyvinyl alcohol resin results by using an isocyanate to prepare the N-(p-cinnamoylphenyl) urethane derivative of PVA.

Reaction of PVA with linseed acids produces unsaturated esters which are polymeric drying "oils" of potential interest to the surface coatings industry, while reaction with polyacrylic acid results in the formation of an insoluble polymeric gel. Graft copolymers are formed by reaction of PVA with acrylonitrile to yield a reduced water-sensitive molecule capable of being spun into fibers or molded.

In aqueous solution reaction with ethylene oxide in the presence of an alkaline catalyst results in the formation of the hydroxyethyl ether. The water vapor permeability of PVA is markedly reduced by reaction with benzyl chloride, the resulting ether having a permeability at 50% etherification—approximately $\frac{1}{10}$ that of PVA.

Cyanoethylation is accomplished by the catalytic reaction of acrylonitrile and PVA in the presence of sodium hydroxide or sodium cyanide, the resulting products being tough, rubbery resins useful in adhesives and coatings. Complete cyanoethylation yields a polymer insoluble in water and chlorinated hydrocarbon solvents but soluble in acetone and methyl acetate. Of possible interest to the analytical chemist is the reaction of PVA with thiourea in heated solution of hydrobromic acid and sodium hydroxide to produce thiol derivatives which with noble metals form mercaptides.

Reaction of PVA with various aldehydes to form the acetals is of considerable industrial importance. Chemicals which react with the hydroxyl group may be used to insolubilize vinyl acetal resins. Thus, glyoxal when added to a vinyl butyral resin in solution during the process of air-drying acts as a curing agent and results in formation of a solvent-resistant film. In that the reaction is reversible in the presence of water, the films are not suitable for water immersion. Cupric ions, especially in the presence of ammonia, insolubilize these resins as do diisocyanates.

VINYL ETHERS

Direct polymerization of vinyl ethers produces polyvinyl ethers:

$$-CH_2-CH-CH_2-CH-CH_2-$$
$$\quad\quad | \quad\quad\quad | $$
$$\quad\quad OR \quad\quad\quad OR$$

The monomeric vinyl ethers are prepared by the addition of alcohols to dilute acetylene in the presence of sodium alkoxides at approximately 30 atmospheres at 150°C. The vinyl ethers are exceptionally reactive compounds which characteristically undergo the reactions of the double bond of vinyl compounds generally. These ethers are readily hydrolyzed by dilute aqueous acids to acetaldehyde and the corresponding alcohols. Ammonia reacts under pressure with vinyl methyl ether to form the substituted pyridines. The monomeric vinyl ethers are hydrogenated in the presence of Raney nickel to the corresponding ethyl ethers, while alcohols add rapidly in the presence of an acid catalyst to form symmetrical and mixed acetals.

Halogenation and the addition of hydrogen halides are extremely vigorous—and sometimes explosive—reactions. Organic acids react with vinyl ethers to yield the corresponding esters. The vinyl ethers contrast with other vinyl monomers in that their polymerization occurs very slowly under the influence of heat or light even in the presence of a catalyst. Polymerization must be carried out by removing the heat of polymerization and under the influence of a mild catalyst. Under favorable conditions the lower vinyl alkyl ethers interpolymerize with many unsaturated compounds. These interpolymers can be prepared by solution, emulsion or bulk methods under the influence of peroxide catalysts and also by ionic or Friedel-Crafts catalysts in anhydrous systems.

Hydrolysis during polymerization in emulsion must be avoided, and thus a pH of 8 or higher is maintained. Copolymers can be made with maleic anhydride, 1,3-dienes, isoprene, styrene, ethylene dicarboxylic acids, various acrylates and methacrylates, acrylic compounds, diolefins, vinyl chloride, ethylene, propylene, butylene, acrylonitrile and chloroprene.

POLYVINYLIDENE CHLORIDE

1,1,2-trichloroethane is pyrolized with the elimination of hydrochloric acid to form asymmetrical dichloroethylene. This monomer (vinylidene chloride) is catalytically converted to the polymer:

$$—CCl_2—CH_2—CCl_2—CH_2—$$

The chemistry of vinylidene chloride polymers is discussed in Chapter 2.

VINYL PYRIDINE

2-and 4-Vinylpyridine are prepared from coal-tar picolines. 2-Vinylpyridine has a boiling point of 71°C. at 18 mm pressure. The material can be polymerized in bulk or in emulsion, and is capable of copolymerization with a number of monomers including isoprene, styrene and butadiene. Heating in the presence of peroxy catalysts at room temperature or slightly above produces hard, tough, transparent resins which are soluble in most organic solvents, producing viscous solutions. Reaction in bulk at elevated temperature forms soft, viscous resins. Emulsion polymerization is commonly carried out with various soaps using a peroxide catalyst. This type of polymerization has been investigated in copolymerization with styrene and butadiene for synthetic rubber applications.

Butadiene copolymers are incompatible with GR-S, but are reported to be superior to GR-S in resistance to tearing and flex cracking. Copolymerization of vinylpyridine with simple alkyl ketones produces ion-exchange resins when copolymerization is effected by a peroxide catalyst. Vinylpyridine copolymers of acrylonitrile readily accept ordinary dyes, and are therefore used in the preparation of acrylic fibers. Acetylene and carbazole combine under conditions of high pressure and catalysis to give the vinyl amine, N-vinylcarbazole.

POLYVINYL STEARATE

The monomer vinyl stearate is a white, waxy solid of melting point 28-30°C.; it can be polymerized to produce polyvinyl stearate:

$$(—CH_2—CH—)_x$$
$$|$$
$$OCOC_{17}H_{35}$$

Polyvinyl stearate exhibits chemical and physical properties characteristic of waxes. Because of the presence of polar groups, it is water-dispersible. Buffered films are water-insensitive and have a high gloss. The polymer is a granular, white, waxy solid melting at 47-48°C.

Copolymerization of vinyl stearate offers some promise as an internal stabilizer. It is reported that copolymers containing 30-45% vinyl stearate and vinyl chloride are internally plasticized. When the concentration of vinyl stearate is approximately 20%, the copolymer of vinyl chloride can be milled at reduced temperatures compared to vinyl chloride homopolymer. Such copolymers are compatible with conventional plasticizers. Copolymerization of vinyl stearate with vinyl acetate is also reported to plasticize internally and also offer greater resistance to hydrolysis than unmodified polyvinyl acetate. Air Reduction Chemical Company states that earlier published work on the polymerization of vinyl stearate indicating that only low polymers are formed is attributed to the presence of vinyl esters of unsaturated acids in the product. It has been found that unsaturation in the acid portion of the molecule retards polymerization. The homopolymer can be formed by suspension, bulk, solution or emulsion methods.

Polymerization in bulk at 70°C. with 0.25% benzoyl peroxide produces a polymer of melting point 45-50°C. It is believed that side chain crystallization occurs. Copolymers may be prepared using oil or water soluble peroxide catalysts and by redox systems. Monomer addition technique of polymerization for the copolymer of vinyl chloride is recommended for high conversion. Copolymers containing up to 20% vinyl stearate are rigid materials. Copolymers containing 10-35% vinyl stearate show a degree of chemical resistance to 1% caustic soda, 50% alcohol and 30% sulfuric acid.

GRAFT COPOLYMERS

The comparatively recent concept of graft copolymerization is receiving increased attention. In the simplest interpretation graft copolymerization involves the addition of a second monomer which is attached to the structure of the already formed polymer. The chain of the homopolymer macromolecule is attacked by the second monomer which is attached in a relatively small number of branches to the polymer.

There are two general methods of grafting of vinyl monomers. The chain transfer method utilizes a monomer which is polymerized in the presence of a polymer. This necessitates that the polymerization be initiated by chain transfer technique. The second method involves the polymerization of a monomer in the presence of a polymer which contains reactive groups or positions along the polymer chain which may be capable of activation to initiate side chain growth. The chain transfer can be accomplished by a free radical generated in a growing chain or from the decomposition of the catalyst used in the polymerization; the free radical removing an atom such as a hydrogen from the growing chain to produce a free radical site for growth of branches.

Radioactive tracer techniques have confirmed the method of attack on the backbone of the molecule, with formation of branched side chains. If the material used to graft on another molecule is dissimilar to that used in the preparation of the original polymer, the resulting polymer is a mixture of pure polymer A (the original polymer), pure polymer B (the second dissimilar monomer added), and a graft polymer which contains branches of polymer B attached to the structure of polymer A. The widely different solubilities of the three constituents enable solvent fractionation to be accomplished in some cases.

Chlorine atoms are potential points of chain transfer just as are hydrogen atoms. It is therefore found that vinyl acetate can be polymerized in the presence of a vinylidene chloride-styrene copolymer, the resulting copolymer containing branches of polyvinyl acetate. Vinyl acetate can be graft-polymerized upon PVC and polyacrylonitrile, but only slight grafting occurs with vinyl acetate or vinyl chloride on polystyrene, or with vinyl chloride on polyvinyl acetate. Styrene shows little grafting tendency on PVC or on polyvinyl acetate. Lower polymerization temperatures lessen the tendency for graft polymerization to occur. This suggests that lower polymerization temperatures decrease the tendency for free radical formation. On the other hand, graft polymerization is promoted by an increase in catalyst concentration. It has been reported that retardation of graft polymerization occurs in polymerization systems involving vinyl chloride and vinyl acetate on polystyrene.

Various types of radiation can be used to effect this polymerization. These radiations may involve photochemical, ultraviolet or sources such as cobalt 60 (gamma rays). Such initiation techniques have been used to graft vinyl acetate on poly(methyl vinyl ketone). Vinyl carbazole grafted on polyethylene retains superior electrical properties, although the polyethylene is considerably stiffened and the softening point appreciably increased.

4. MANUFACTURE AND FABRICATION

POLYVINYL CHLORIDE

Types of Polymerization

Four commercial methods for polymerization of vinyl chloride monomer have been used: in bulk (mass), in solution, in emulsion and in suspension. The last now constitutes the mode of preparation for the majority of the polymer prepared in the United States.

Bulk polymerization has been investigated in both this country and abroad. In conventional mass polymerization the monomer forms a solid or semi-solid state. Cobalt 60 has been studied as an unconventional initiator for the preparation of bulk polymer. Theoretically this offers much, because under suitable conditions the presence of conventional catalysts and other normal polymerization ingredients are unnecessary, and no drying of product is required. However, at this time it is believed that these experimentations in radioactive initiation of the vinyls are not feasible. In addition to the usual difficulties encountered in bulk polymerization, the radioactive initiator requires extensive shielding of the reactor to prevent radiation injury to plant personnel. This objection probably could be offset if the cost of the product so prepared would be competitive. Examination has not shown any appreciable advantage over cheaper methods of preparation.

Emulsion polymer is currently regaining some of its lost

volume in that plastisol and organisol applications are increasing. The cost of preparation of emulsion PVC is in excess of that made by suspension methods. Much of this cost lies in the large capital investment necessitated by spray driers. Polymer obtained by emulsion is materially different from that made by suspension methods. Emulsion polymer is not wet by plasticizers to the degree characteristic of suspension resin. This permits such uses as slush molding and various paste applications. Emulsion polymer is much smaller in particle size than suspension resin, the former being in the low micron range. Emulsion polymerization of monomer in water is activated by persulfate or other catalysts using any of many emulsifying agents.

Emulsion Polymerization

In the emulsion polymerization of vinyl chloride, a number of catalysts have been reported. Among these are benzoyl peroxide, hydrogen peroxide, potassium and ammonium persulfate, various perborates and percarbonates and calcium and barium peroxides. Emulsifiers promote intimate contact between the dispersed monomer and the water-soluble catalyst. Recently nonionic emulsifiers have become increasingly prominent, as these materials are relatively unaffected by various salts and hard water. Anionic surfactants are still prominent and include various sulfonic and sulfonated hydrocarbons, alkyl naphthalene sulfonic acids and sulfonated castor oil. Emulsion polymerization requires the presence of relatively large quantities of protective colloids such as PVA, hydroxyethyl cellulose, carboxymethyl cellulose, alginates and other materials in order that the latex may be stable. This is of prime importance in the preparation of latex paints, among the first of which was styrene-butadiene copolymer emulsion. Recently polyvinyl acetate as well as various acrylic polymers and copolymers have become prominent in this field.

The emulsifier content used in the preparation of emulsion

(dispersion) resins may be as high as 5% of the resin content. Sodium lauryl sulfate is often used in combination with lauroyl peroxide as the catalyst. At the conclusion of the polymerization the reaction products are stripped by removing unreacted monomer and the latex spray-dried without preliminary coagulation and washing, as was formally practiced. Unlike suspension PVC, the drying of emulsion resins is critical, since particle size, particle size distribution, and residual moisture all are of importance. Emulsion resins must quickly disperse in the plasticizer and form a dispersion of low initial viscosity so that high solids concentration can be readily processed. It is also a requirement that the viscosity of the resin not appreciably decrease during aging.

The particle size of the latex is of considerable importance in the preparation of dispersion resins. The mechanical stability of the latex must be sufficient to prevent mechanical shock or agitation from causing coagulation; otherwise, coagulation may occur during transportation and storage. It is essential the latex have a certain minimum stability if it is to be used in spray-drying systems. Stability is imparted to some degree by the concentration of emulsifier present. Dispersion resins have poorer electrical resistivity than suspension resins, and this weakness is intensified by the presence of emulsifying agent. Some manufacturers add additional emulsifier at the end of the polymerization to the latex to prevent premature separation of the polymer before spray-drying. Some emulsifying agents impart a degree of heat stabilization. Sodium stearate, for example, does this when the spray-drying retains the emulsifier in the finished material.

The principle of "seed" polymerization is sometimes employed in polymerizing vinyls in emulsion. This technique is used when large polymer particles of uniform size are desired. It involves the addition of a previously prepared polymer latex to a second polymerization when the reactants are first charged. Polymerization occurs upon the nuclei of the previous polymerization, provided excessive amounts of emulsifying agent are not used. The polymer latex which results from the seeding technique can then be used as seed material for further polymerizations.

The addition of large quantities of emulsifying agent in the polymerization charge can be avoided by a specialized technique. Water, vinyl chloride and catalysts are charged into an evacuated reactor and the mixture stirred with heating to 125°F. After one or two hours' time the conversion of monomer is approximately 1%. At this time a quantity of a metallic salt of a sulfonated fatty acid or ester is added and polymerization continued until the concentration of polymer is approximately 30%. The finished latex is of good mechanical stability and a uniform particle size of about 0.5 micron in diameter results. If further mechanical stability is desired for spray-drying or other reasons, more emulsifier can be added to the finished latex. The water absorption and power factor of the dispersion resin is increased as the quantity of emulsifying agent is increased, but electrical resistivity is lowered.

Solution Polymerization

Solution polymerization in an inert solvent is believed to be used to a great extent by only one U. S. manufacturer, and that primarily in copolymers. Suspension polymer has the significant advantage of quick separation from the water diluent; it is easily washed, if desired, centrifuged and dried in rotary driers. Costly spray drying is unnecessary. In addition to the economics favoring use of the suspension process, a superior PVC can be made by this method.

PVC described here will be limited to suspension and emulsion resins due to the relative unimportance of bulk polymer and the limitedly used solution process. Suspension and emulsion methods for the manufacture of PVC far outstrip bulk and solution preparation in importance.

Suspension Polymerization

Suspension PVC is prepared using any of a number of different suspension agents. It is believed that for the most part a single suspension material only is used in a given preparation. Among these materials are methyl cellulose, sodium carboxymethyl cellulose, ethyl cellulose, various gelatins and polyvinyl alcohols. Gelatin, PVA and methyl cellulose are probably most widely used. In addition to these materials, limited use of other materials has been made. These include interpolymers such as methacrylic acid and methyl methacrylate, and protenoid substances including zein and casein.

The properties of suspension PVC show a wide variation among manufacturers. This can be due to a great number of variables in the polymerization system: for example, the ratio of monomer to water, particular suspending agent employed, the possible inclusion of various emulsifiers, buffers and other additives, choice and amount of catalyst used, type of agitation employed, speed of agitation, heat transfer of the reactor, temperature of polymerization and other factors. In addition to all these, minor amounts of materials used to terminate polymerization (isoprene) have an effect as well as those used to chain-transfer. In essentially unmodified polyvinyl chloride some manufacturers do employ minor amounts of copolymerizing ingredients. These may include vinylidene chloride, various maleates, acetates, acrylates and chlorinated materials.

Preparation of polyvinyl chloride described in the older literature frequently referred to suspension polymerization requiring up to several days at 40-55°C. before polymerization was essentially complete. Most commercial PVC manufactured in this country today by suspension processes requires under 24 hours to prepare high molecular weight products. The products are white, free-flowing powders of varying particle size. Uniformity of particle size is desired by all manufacturers, but seldom attained by most. In general, fine particle size is produced because of the tendency for insoluble gels to result in coarser polymer made by most, but not all manufacturers. It is a decided advantage to most resin fabricators to use coarse PVC if the resin manufacturer can supply such of excellent quality.

Suspension PVC, when processed into film or sheeting, gives a product of superior properties to material made from dispersion resin. Film clarity is much superior and gel count is materially lower with suspension grade resin. In electrical applications gels reduce the dielectric strength so that the material is subject to a lower break-down voltage. The suspension polymerization system most often used is composed of a reactor charge of monomer, water, catalyst, suspending agent, emulsifying agent, and sometimes buffers. Water-soluble suspending and emulsifying agents are usually used in conjunction, as both these materials result in a finished resin of lower gel count. The ratio of water to vinyl chloride monomer is varied from 2 to 5:1. The suspending agent may be as low as 0.01 to 0.5% based on the weight of the monomer.

The emulsifier is never used in concentrations as great as the suspending agent, but this also has a variation of some ten fold, being present in concentrations from 0.01 to 0.1%. The oil-soluble peroxide catalyst most often used is lauroyl peroxide in concentrations of as little as 0.1% and rarely exceeding 0.5%. Nonionic emulsifiers are employed, and the colloidal suspending agents most often used are gelatin, methyl cellulose or polyvinyl alcohol.

The ingredients are charged to a glass-lined pressure vessel, the largest of which is believed to be of 3700-gallon capacity. These pressure vessels vary in design and geometry, but generally use glass agitators and baffles. The reactor is purged of oxygen of the atmosphere by a succession of evacuations purging with excess vinyl chloride and possibly an inert gas. A commonly used reaction temperature is 122°F. throughout the polymerization cycle. This temperature is maintained by automatic control equipment which provides the proper flow of steam and cooling water into the jacket of the reactor.

(*Courtesy Escambia Chemical Corporation*)

Figure 4.1. A section of vinyl chloride polymerization reactors.

In general suspension polymerization for high molecular weight polymer requires a charging time of about 1 hr, polymerization of 12-16 hr and a blowdown transfer time of 1-2 hr depending upon the finishing operation. The conversion of monomer to polymer is quite low during the early hours of the reaction cycle and in many formulations is less than 30% after 6 hours' reaction time. Since the reaction is exothermic (-720 Btu per pound), heat has to be removed from the reactor during the polymerization. Good heat transfer is necessary when the rates of conversion become high with a corresponding high exotherm. Cooling water must then be supplied rapidly. When the rate of conversion is a maximum, it is accompanied by incipient pressure drop during this "peak" time. Little monomer is converted to polymer after a conversion of some 90% has been obtained. It is generally true that the bulk density of polymer increases with time of polymerization. Unmodified PVC prepared by the above described method when the polymerization is terminated at less than 50% conversion is of a bulk density often less than 20 lb/cu ft. This polymer quite characteristically shows a very high plasticizer absorption. In some operations the pressure drop is allowed to proceed to 40-50 lb (from about 100 psig at 122°F.) before the polymer is blown down from the reactor.

The blow-down tank receives the polymer and the residual monomer. The monomer is stripped for use in other reactor charges. A portion of the monomer is removed through the monomer recovery system and the remainder by vacuum jets. In some older PVC plants, foaming is a considerable problem in monomer recovery when the vapor pressure is less than 20 psig. These plants sometimes employ an antifoam agent to minimize the monomer recovery difficulty. After the monomer recovery is complete, the polymer is transferred to blend tanks followed by centrifugation. The polymer may be washed with water in continuous centrifuges. This practice varies among different manufacturers as some concerns use little or no washing. The reason for this is perhaps an economy of operation as well as permitting certain ingredients, notably buffers, to remain in the finished polymer. The moisture content of the polymer as it leaves the centrifuge varies over a rather wide limit depending upon the type of centrifuge and the nature of the polymer which is processed.

Generally a water content of about 25% or less is delivered to the driers. Rotary driers are most often employed. The ingoing temperature is 300°F. for PVC and the outgoing temperature about 150°F. The minimum temperature which can be used and deliver a finished product of a maximum volatile content of 0.5% is desired. The resin is collected in a vertical felt cylinder and the resin adhering to the sides is removed by an air jet. From this the polymer is delivered by gravity into the conical bottom of the collector, passed through a 40 mesh screen, conveyed to storage bins, analyzed to meet all quality specifications and finally packed in 50 lb multi-ply paper bags.

(*Courtesy Escambia Chemical Corporation*)

Figure 4.2. View of PVC centrifuges and rotary driers.

As was discussed elsewhere, it is essential that the monomer be without impurities and substantially free of phenol inhibitor. The distillation of the monomer to remove inhibitor must be carefully controlled. The presence of dissolved air in the charge water or from improper purging of the reactor delays initiation of polymerization. Excessive amounts of catalyst which decompose to yield molecular oxygen also result in longer polymerization time. A judicious choice of the catalyst concentration must be made as excessive amounts of catalyst as well as poor temperature control can cause variation in the desired average molecular weight. The presence of excessive catalyst in the polymerization system results in a polymer of poor color and decreased heat stability.

POLYVINYL ACETATE

Three general methods are known for the commercial preparation of polyvinyl acetate—by dispersion, solution and bulk polymerization. In latex or emulsion polymerization vinyl

(Courtesy Air Reduction Chemical Company)

Figure 4.3. Vinyl acetate monomer plant.

acetate is polymerized in the presence of a catalyst, water, a protective colloid and a surface active agent. Stable, milky-white emulsions result which are 50-60% solids. A second method for polymerization by dispersion is the formation of bead polymers. The ingredients in the bead polymerization are equivalent to those in emulsion except the product which is formed is in a form of small beads and is readily separated from the water. An aldehyde is often used in the reaction mixture as a control of the molecular weight of the polymer.

Polyvinyl acetate latices are manufactured by a batch method using two variations. In one case, the entire monomer charge is added to the reactor at the beginning, and in the other method only a small amount of monomer is charged initially and the majority which remains is added increment-wise during the course of the polymerization. This latter method can be made continuous by pumping the reactants through a series of kettles.

A typical charge is described as follows:

	Parts by Weight
Vinyl acetate	100
Water	103
Hydrogen peroxide (30%)	0.5
Polyvinyl alcohol ("Elvanol," 71-24)	5.0
Gum tragacanth	0.5

When all the monomer is charged initially, the PVA is added to the water and well dispersed. The addition of the vinyl acetate is made with constant agitation but at such a rate that excessive foaming does not result. Gum tragacanth is added and the contents of the reactor heated to 60°C. at which time hydrogen peroxide is charged and the temperature elevated to 65°C. At this temperature a steady reflux results and polymerization is initiated. The heat of polymerization is sufficient to carry out the reaction without the addition of further heating.

After the polymerization reaches a high conversion, the temperature falls and it is then necessary to add heat to maintain a steady reflux until the temperature reaches 90°C. Outside heating is stopped and the agitation is continued until the latex reaches room temperature and transfer can then be made from the reactor to storage. It is essential that agitation be maintained until a temperature of 35°C. is obtained, or surface skinning will result.

The batch process is difficult to control and a reproducible uniform latex is hard to obtain. In a modification of the batch process by continuous monomer addition the PVA is added to the water and well dispersed, vinyl acetate then added to an amount of 5-15% of the total monomer charge and the gum is introduced. After the temperature reaches 60°C. the catalyst is charged and eventually heating discontinued and a steady reflux obtained. Heating to 90°C., as in the single charge of monomer, is ultimately obtained. The latices produced from either of these batch methods are creamy, white dispersions free from lumps and sandy particles. A typical latex will contain 57-59% solids and less than 0.7% monomeric vinyl acetate. The absolute viscosity is 5-50 poises at 20°C., the resin solution viscosity is 3.5 to 10.0 centipoises at 20°C., and the pH 4-5. The latices so manufactured generally have average particle sizes between 0.5 and 1.5 microns.

When hydroxyethyl cellulose is used as a protective colloid the latex has excellent stability and produces air-dried films which are resistant to re-emulsification. Such a colloid is especially suitable for use in water-base paints. Polyvinyl alcohol as a protective colloid forms latices which are better suited to adhesive applications. These have high solvent tolerance, good tack and good mechanical stability. The water resistance of latices using polyvinyl alcohol as a colloid is not as high as that of latices prepared with hydroxyethyl cellulose.

A formulation supplied by Union Carbide using "Cellosize" hydroxyethyl cellulose is described as follows:

Ingredients	Parts by Weight	Laboratory Charges
Vinyl acetate HQ	55.5	944.0 g
Water	42.0	713.5
"Cellosize" WP-09	1.0	17.0
"Cellosize" WP-300	1.0	17.0
Tergitol dispersant NPX	0.15	2.55
Potassium persulfate	0.20	3.40
Sodium bicarbonate	0.15	2.55
Total	100.00	1700.00 g

All the ingredients except the vinyl acetate and the sodium bicarbonate are charged to a flask. The mixture is agitated and heat is applied by circulating hot water through the bath. When complete solution of the "Cellosize" WP-09 and "Cellosize" WP-300 is effected, about 5% of the vinyl acetate is added and the mixture is agitated moderately (300 to 400 rpm) with continued heating. Air in the system is displaced by purging with nitrogen, and a blanket of nitrogen is maintained during the entire polymerization to prevent the re-entry of traces of air into the system. The polymerization of the monomer in the charge is substantially complete by the time the reflux temperature of vinyl acetate and water (67°C.) is reached. The heating is continued until a temperature of 70°C. is attained, at which point the remaining vinyl acetate is slowly added.

The rate of addition of vinyl acetate is such as to permit the maintenance of a 75 to 80°C. temperature with little or no reflux. About two hours is required for the addition of the monomer. After all the vinyl acetate has been added, the temperature of the reaction mixture is raised to 85°C. The addition of 0.01% potassium persulfate catalyst followed by heating for 30 min. at this temperature is usually sufficient to reduce the monomer content of the latex to 1% or less. There are indications that more complete reaction is obtained if the reaction temperature is held below 78°C. (e.g. 73-78°C.) for a half-hour or so after all the monomer has been added and the mixture cooled. Additional catalyst may or may not be required. The latex is adjusted to the proper pH range (4 to 5) by the addition of powdered sodium bicarbonate. Formation of thick, leathery skins on the surface of the latex is prevented by continuing the agitation while the product is being cooled to room temperature by circulating cold water through the cooling bath.

U.S.P. 2,508,341 (Shawinigan Resins) describes a process for the preparation of polyvinyl acetate latices with hydroxyethyl cellulose as the protective colloid.

A number of factors affect the manufactured properties of polyvinyl acetate. The catalyst which is used has a profound effect upon the rate of polymerization. The amount of the catalyst in the polymerization system affects not only the molecular weight of the resin but the viscosity of the latex. Increased amounts of catalyst tend to lower the molecular weight of the resin and to some extent lower the viscosity of the latex.

Increased amounts of protective colloid also increase the viscosity of the latex. This increase in the colloid concentration may also decrease the particle size. Poor latex stability can be caused by insufficient colloid, but excessive quantities of protective colloid will result in too high a viscosity. The more monomer present initially in the reaction mixture, the higher the molecular weight of the finished resin. The molecular weight is also increased by increasing the rate of monomer addition.

There are indications that polyvinyl acetate of improved water resistance is prepared by maintaining very low concentrations of unreacted monomer during polymerization. The ratio of water to monomer is of considerable importance. This ratio naturally controls the total solids and thus has an effect on the latex viscosity. A low resin-to-water ratio tends to produce small particles and low molecular weight. The usual operating temperature is of the order of 70-85°C. If the reaction temperature is maintained at the higher part of this temperature range, the viscosity increases and particle size and molecular weight decrease.

Potassium persulfate is an effective catalyst when used in concentrations of 0.3 to 0.4% based on the monomer charge. At such concentrations of catalyst the latex will be of a low pH (approximately 2.5-3.5). This catalyst must be neutralized so that it will not decompose to sulfuric acid which would promote the hydrolysis of polyvinyl acetate, with subsequent build up of acetic acid. Sodium bicarbonate adjusts the pH to 4-6 to prevent this decomposition. Hydrogen peroxide is a more effective catalyst when the reaction vessel is made of stainless steel than if a glass-lined reactor is used.

Surfactants are of both anionic and nonionic types. The sodium salts of alkyl aryl sulfonates have been used. An efficient commercial reactor is a 1000-gallon glass-lined vessel. Jacketed stainless steel vessels may also be used to prepare emulsions of polyvinyl acetate, but the use of this type of equipment may present a greater cleaning problem. Water emulsions of polyvinyl acetate may be stored in contact with most surfaces except mild steel and copper. Wood, stainless steel, aluminum, phenolic-coated steels, and glass are satisfactory materials. Solution polymerization of vinyl acetate is effected in the presence of a solvent to yield a solution of the polymer. Molecular weight regulators may or may not be used. In bulk polymerization the monomer is polymerized in the presence of a catalyst and a molecular weight regulator. In this type of polymerization no solvents or diluents are employed.

The fabricator of polyvinyl acetate finds that the preferred method of making solutions is to add the polymer granules to the solvent while stirring fast enough to keep the resin from settling to the bottom of the container, and continuing this agitation until solution is complete. If agitation is too slow or is temporarily discontinued before solution is complete, the polyvinyl acetate will settle to the bottom and coalesce. If the mixer employed is of a slow, heavy-duty type, soaking the polyvinyl acetate in the solvent for some hours followed by agitation for a short time is preferred. The solutions are usually prepared at room temperature, but the time required is reduced by heating. This heating should be performed in a closed mixer equipped with a reflux condenser.

It is important that emulsions of polyvinyl acetate not be allowed to freeze. After long storage or freezing there may be phase separation and the resin may coalesce in the bottom of the container and perhaps cannot be redispersed.

The greatest volume of polyvinyl acetate resins is now sold in the form of emulsions. This large volume preparation is used chiefly for paint vehicles, textile finishes, adhesives and coatings. The growing acceptance of polyvinyl acetate emulsions for interior and exterior paint accounts for large volume usage. Use in paint in 1956 in the United States was 10.5 million gallons.

Solution polymerization may be carried out in solvents such as benzene, toluene, ethyl acetate or ethanol by refluxing the monomer in the presence of 0.1-0.5% of a catalyst such as benzoyl peroxide, lauroyl peroxide or acetyl peroxide. Depending upon the choice of solvent and catalyst and the amounts of each employed and upon other conditions, such as temperature and the presence of chain transfer agents, polymers of widely varying molecular weights can be obtained. Polymers produced by such solution methods are generally of low molecular weight. Polyvinyl acetate prepared in solution finds major outlets as adhesives, binders and coatings. The solid polymer may be recovered by evaporation of the solvent. These solids, usually in the form of beads, may be converted to polyvinyl alcohol or to polyvinyl acetals.

Vinyl acetate is frequently copolymerized or terpolymerized with other vinyl monomers in emulsion systems to improve such properties as flexibility, adhesion and water resistance.

This approach is preferred to the use of additives which do not enter chemically into the polymer when greater permanence of specific properties is desired. Modifiers can be included in emulsion polymerization systems to terminate propagating polymer chains. The concentration of such modifiers determines the final molecular weight of the polymers so obtained. In addition to controlling molecular weight such modifiers can prevent or reduce branching and/or cross-linking. These modifiers may be chlorinated aliphatics, aldehydes or mercaptans. Glycols are frequently added to latex to improve freeze-thaw stability, while tricresyl phosphate imparts flameproofing properties.

VINYL FABRICATION

Dry Blending

Dry blending is of particular interest to the extruder of PVC. Many advantages accompany the preparation of a dry, sandy blend of resins, plasticizers, stabilizers, lubricants and fillers. Use of resins which permit preparation of a free-flowing powder give lower conversion costs and in some cases increased extrusion rates of the dry blend; lower equipment costs in that conventional heavy compounding equipment is eliminated; a reduced heat history which permits preparation of higher quality products; and lastly, better uniformity of the fabricated product.

The most widely accepted method of dry blending involves the addition of dry components consisting of fillers and possibly stabilizers (if solids) to a jacketed ribbon blender containing the heated resin. Liquid components consisting of plasticizers, lubricants and stabilizers are mixed in a suitable strip heater or steam-jacketed vessel and transferred from this vessel to the ribbon blender. In some operations the dry ingredients are added after the plasticizer and other components. The ribbon blender is heated so that the temperature of the resin ingredients is in excess of 100°C. After the complete absorption of plasticizer, steam is turned off the jacket and cold circulating water is turned on; the temperature of the resin constituents is reduced to about room temperature, and the dry blend dumped and screened. An even shorter cycle is provided by a "Speedmullor" in place of the ribbon blender. Another mixer which is used is an internal mixer such as the Beken mixer.

Dry blending resins offer certain savings in processing, particularly in extrusion. An older method of processing which is still used to a considerable extent is the addition of all the ingredients to a ribbon blender followed by mixing at various temperatures in an internal mixer, sheeting on heated mills and finally, dicing or granulation of the product prior to extrusion. The dry blending technique permits the product to be supplied to the extruder directly from the ribbon blender with obvious savings in time and equipment. The shortened period of time and heat history can permit a better product to be fabricated. Depending upon the resin and requirements of the finished product, the dry blending technique can sometimes produce faster extrusion rates.

Fisheyes

The causes of gels in fabricated vinyls lie in the resin preparation and the manner that this resin is processed. Perhaps the greater responsibility lies with the resin manufacturer, though this is certainly not the entire reason for this difficulty. Fisheyes are particularly noticeable in the form of localized blemishes in pigmented film or sheeting. A number of reasons for excessive fisheyes can be advanced. The uneven absorption of plasticizer during the blending, and in particular dry blending of resin, can produce a high fisheye count. This may result from nonuniformity of particle size and shape as well as variations in molecular weight, particle porosity, cross-linking and contamination of the resin.

Perhaps the foremost reason for gel difficulties is due to the variation in plastic flow of the gel caused by under-plasticization of the gel particle. It has been stated that coarse particles are the primary reason for fisheyes in that they cannot compete with fine particles for plasticizer. This is not necessarily the case. Carefully selected polymerization recipes and conditions of resin preparation can produce relatively coarse product (appreciable retention of resin on 80 mesh screen) which is not only free of objectionable dust but a resin of unusually low gel count. It is also stated by some that a low gel count cannot be obtained without short-stopping of the resin by some agent so that post-polymerization is prevented.

Again this is not necessary under the proper conditions of resin preparation. The mere preparation of unusually fine resin is not the answer to the fisheye problem in that some resin, unusually fine in particle size, manufactured in this country also possesses the highest gel counts. Some of these very fine commercial resins have a high degree of solvation by the plasticizer, and yet have many particles which absorb little or no plasticizer; thus a high gel count results.

Vinyl Calendering

Easy processing is a major factor in the calendering of vinyl resins. In the simplest analysis of the calendering process, the complete cycle consists of pre-mixing, internal mixing, milling, calendering, cooling and wind-up. Ribbon blenders are often employed in pre-mixing and batch sizes 4,000 lb or more are sometimes made. Resins are used which can be pre-mixed cold, while others require steam-jacketed blenders in order to obtain a dry pre-blend. Cold pre-mixing resins have a disadvantage of very low bulk density which decreases the throughput on a pound-volume basis, but they do offer the economy of not requiring heating in this operation. The plasticizer and other ingredients added in the pre-

mixing cycle are heated to about 200°F., at which temperature they are delivered by gravity feed to the internal mixer.
A heated pre-mix decreases the mixing cycle required in a
Banbury, with resulting economy. The pigments are most
often added to the internal mixer to decrease cleaning problems which would be necessary if the colorants are added in
the blender. The action of heat and mechanical shearing
allow thorough blending and fusion of the reactants.

An often used internal mixer charge is 175 lb, which requires a mixing cycle not in excess of 6 minutes and often
substantially less. The stock temperature in the internal mixer
is 275-300°F. An excellent method of delivery of the internally mixed charge is by gravity to heated mills. Modern
calendering plants use two mills or an extruder to feed the
calender. The temperature of the mills depends upon the
gauge and type of stock employed. The milling temperature
is usually somewhat below the maximum Banbury temperature.

Some calenders in the vinyl industry are still rubber calenders; however, these are rapidly being replaced by more
modern machines. The current trend is toward four-roll
calenders, the majority of which are inverted-L, although
some recent installations are of a Z-type. Calender roll temperatures for film are a maximum of about 340°F. and 370°F.
or more for sheeting. These high temperatures require not
only the use of heat stabilizers for the resin but PVC and
vinyl copolymers of the best possible inherent heat stability.
Good heat stability is required as substantial quantities of
scrap are obtained from the calender trim edges, all of which
must be reworked for the best economy of operation. Modern
calenders are often operated at speeds of 100 yards or more
per minute for film production. Such high speeds require the
best of gauge control and uniform temperatures across the
calender rolls. It is now characteristic to emboss film or
sheeting continuously in the calendering operation. At the

completion of the calendering cycle the vinyl is cooled and wound with a minimum stress to prevent shrinkage of the wrapped product.

(Courtesy Adamson United Company)

Figure 4.4. 28″ x 74″ 4-roll inverted-Ell calender.

A modern calender which can operate at temperatures as high as 550°F. was installed in 1957 by Kaye-Tex Manufacturing Company. Built by Adamson United Company, it can produce material of gauges from 2½ to 40 mils. This four-roll machine is of the bow-bending type which permits calendering of various gauges without changing the rollers. This calender will be fed by a continuous 12-inch flux extruder. The most modern calenders weigh in excess of 200,000 lb and are capable of producing 12,000 yards of vinyl sheeting per hour up to 72 inches wide.

Calender "Plate Out"

Recent work developed by Bakelite on roll plating finds that this phenomenon is directly proportional to the barium-cadmium stabilizer concentration. "Plate out" involves the deposition of a coating on the rolls of the calender. This coating results in a poor surface of the film or sheeting, and also makes sheet transfer from roll to roll difficult and consequently reduces production rate. Plating is also influenced in compounding formulations by such variables as resins, lubricants, pigments and chelating agents; but all these are believed to be of less importance than the presence of barium-cadmium stabilizers. The higher the concentration of this stabilizer, the more severe the plating. It is found that barium-cadmium laurates are particularly objectionable. It is reported that plating is more severe when the barium content of the stabilizer is greater than cadmium.

Coated Fabrics

The coated fabric industry in 1956 had sales in excess of $100,000,000 per year for end uses. Three fabrics are used in coating—woven, knitted, and nonwoven. Pyroxylin-coated fabrics still find major outlets for bookbinding applications, while vinyl-coated fabrics are used where superior flexing and abrasion resistance are required. The majority of vinyl coatings applied by either knife or reverse roll are dispersion resins applied as an organosol, plastisol or latex. The organosol solids are a usual minimum of 60%. In plastisol coatings stir-in mixing of the dispersion resin, plasticizer and other ingredients is made. The usual method of coating is a knife operation at 350°F. The embossing and wind-up are similar to that employed in the calendering process. When mineral spirits are used to reduce plastisol viscosity, the thinner must be removed at a temperature lower than the fusion temperature before the resin is cured. It is necessary that the plastisol mixture be of a low solvating type so that good viscosity shelf life is provided, although a high-solvating plasticizer must be used in conjunction to give better fusion at elevated temperatures.

Vinyl-coated fabric is a rapidly growing field of major

importance. In earlier days fabrication was primarily concerned with simulating leather, and the term "leather cloth" was applied. Dispersion and suspension resins are used in vinyl-coated fabric applications. The plastisol is spread onto the cloth as a fluid paste, the excess removed and the resin converted by subsequent heating to a flexible coating. The method of calendering suspension resin as film and sheeting onto the fabric is gaining in popularity and represents the largest mode of processing of coated fabric. Maximum strength is developed by heating PVC-coated fabric by processing the laminate over a series of rolls which also are used to transfer dyes and inks onto the coating surface. Embossing is applied by heating the coated fabric and passing the material under an engraved roll.

A major outlet for coated fabrics is in upholstery, a large portion of the material being used in public transport including aircraft and railways. The coated fabrics are used for chair coverings, stools and desk coverings. Wall coverings, footwear, bookbindings, handbags and luggage are other major applications. Approximately 35% of calendered vinyl sheeting in 1957 was used in coated fabric applications.

Radio-frequency welding of PVC-coated fabrics is of prime importance. Quality application of PVC-coated fabrics in the luggage industry is a major business. Unsupported PVC sheeting is widely used in the handbag industry and in clothing and the fabrication of various jacket wear. Coated fabrics for chairs have been aided by the manufacture of PVC which has a discontinuous coating which permits the material to "breathe." These small openings provide aeration and increased seating comfort. The higher water vapor transmission rate of leather in footwear over PVC permits better breathing properties of leather. This factor has impeded the use of PVC in footwear, although ladies' and infants' shoes in particular do find application. In wall coverings the vinyl is often applied by bonding to various backing materials to produce a highly scuff-proof and decorative purpose.

Vinyl-coated fabrics of unsupported types were first used in luggage in 1947. The delay in the use of this type of material was due to an adhesive problem. The Marvibond process has been of value; it consists of sheet metal to which film made from rigid to semi-rigid resin compounds is firmly laminated on one or both sides. The plastic film used in this construction employs a high molecular weight PVC which is more chemically resistant and heat-stable than the solution-grade vinyl copolymer resins. Spraying from solution is not practical or economical due to pronounced webbing when solids greater than 10% by weight are used and the high cost of solvents.

The luggage industry has bonded vinyl sheeting, either smooth or embossed and either continuously or in sheet, to a light metal such as magnesium. Injection molding, extrusion, vacuum and post-forming techniques are also used. Luggage covering must withstand temperature ranges from 20°F. below zero to 200°F. The film or sheeting must not warp, shrink, discolor or crack within this wide temperature range. The luggage surface must be hard and snag-resistant and must have high abrasion resistance and tensile strength. The luggage industry is now predominantly of a non-leather type and is rapidly growing. Purchases of film and supported and non-supported sheeting for luggage is about $7,000,000 a year.

A support for vinyl in automobile upholstery which is growing in popularity is an application of nonwoven bonded fabrics as a backing for vinyl-coated upholstery. The textile fibers of the nonwoven fabric are bonded using vinyl latex. Use of the latex imparts maximum strength, resilience and flexibility and provides an excellent material to which vinyl sheet may be calendered.

Injection Molding of PVC

The typical volume resistivity for PVC of 1×10^{13} ohm-cm at 50°C. makes PVC attractive to injection molders due to its insulating characteristics and ease of application in the manufacture of outlet plugs, various insulators, battery clips, etc.

The role of PVC in wire coverings has been discussed elsewhere (pp. 180-186). The widespread application of PVC in wire and cable insulation is augmented by its use in injection molding of parts for various electrical appliances. The flexibility and adequate performance at low temperatures, resistance to deformation, oil and chemical resistance, excellent electrical properties, high abrasion and scuff resistance, high tear strength, low shrinkage and approval for some uses up to 105°C. all contribute to the popularity of PVC in molding applications. This volume application in 1957 is estimated at 7 million pounds of resin.

The composition of the ingredients used in formulation of compound for injection molding is varied to suit the end use application. The resin content is sometimes as low as 60% and is coupled with a wide variety of plasticizers, stabilizers, fillers, pigments and lubricants. The amount and type of plasticizer varies depending upon whether the application is to be at low or high temperatures. Adipates and sebacates are used for cold applications while the less volatile phthalates and phosphates find application for higher-temperature service. Lead stabilizers are used as well as barium-cadmium compounds and epoxy stabilizers. It is generally advisable to avoid the use of lead salts in the molding of any appliance which will be used in kitchen appliances because of the toxic nature of the lead compounds and sulfur cross-staining. The lead salts are also replaced in the preparation of clear or translucent compounds.

PVC either in the plasticized dry blend or pelletized forms can be used in injection molding. Pellets are made after the compounded resin has been internally mixed, milled, the strips cut from the mill after complete fusion and then diced. The easy-processing resins offer advantages in decreasing the capital outlay required by minimizing the amount of equipment necessary. Certain other advantages of the dry blend are also found, such as the ease of filling complex contoured molds, and the lesser heat history required in processing versus diced material.

Injection molding of unplasticized PVC has recently become more attractive economically. Conventional molding equipment can be used in which the polymer is heated in the cylinder to a temperature of approximately 10°F. below the flow temperature, and the polymer forced through a narrow passage preceding the nozzle. Transfer molding of rigid PVC is finding increased application. Flexible vinyls containing greater than 20% plasticizer can be readily injection-molded in conventional machinery. This permits much lower temperatures than in rigid applications, and in these plasticizer systems there is little danger of thermal decomposition of the polymer. Pressures slightly in excess of 20 psi can be used to force the PVC into a mold heated at 50°C. Rigid PVC is stabilized at a level of about 2% based on the PVC. The use of stabilizers is essential in decreasing the thermal decomposition and it is advisable to use corrosion resistant alloys in the molding machine. There are indications that American industry in the future will rely on lower molecular weight suspension PVC for rigid injection molding.

Extrusion

The extrusion of vinyl plastics is a field of great and growing importance. PVC may be extruded in a rigid or flexible composition, the rigid compound containing generally no more than 3% stabilizers and possibly lubricants and fillers. Plasticized vinyl is extruded from single or twin screw extruders. Articles of various shapes and profiles, garden hose, wire coating, blown film and sheeting and monofilament are all major outlets.*

The extrusion of film and sheeting is relatively small in volume and may be accomplished either through a flat film die or a circular blown film die. Perhaps the preferred method of film extrusion is by use of a circular die followed by inflation with compressed air and a hot stretch. The extrusion of monofilament will be discussed in chapter 5. A rapidly growing development is the extrusion of highly plasticized tubing for medical and beverage applications. Plasticizers which are approved by the Food and Drug Administration are used in conjunction with nontoxic stabilizers. Some extrusions of vinyl tubing for use in intravenous applications are made in a totally unstabilized system.

A general description of the art of vinyl extrusion could be made in the category of garden hose. Of somewhat greater complexity and larger volume is the extrusion of wire and cable. In its simplest concept this involves a reel of wire which may or may not be heated and passed through an extruder cross-head, followed by a cooling trough, spark tester, capstan, and reel take-up. Thorough fluxing is provided the vinyl resin in the heating cylinder of the extruder and the material screw-conveyed toward screen packings.

The capstan pulls the vinyl-coated wire through the cooling trough at a speed sufficient to give the desired outside diameter of the insulation. The spark tester is used as a measure of quality control and ultimately the wire is wound onto reels for delivery. Compression ratios are generally lower when extrusion of granules is made and higher for powder blend material. These compression ratios are often as low as 1.5/1 for granulated plastic and as high as 4.0/1

* The book "Extrusion of Plastics, Rubber, and Metals" by Simonds and Weith (Reinhold, 1952), adequately describes basic vinyl extrusion. The "Plastics Engineering Handbook" (Reinhold, 1954), is another excellent reference broadly covering this field.

for dry blended resin. Older extruders were steam-heated, but this type of heating system has been replaced by oil or electricity which permit higher operational temperatures without excessive pressures. Certain advantages are offered by electric and oil heating systems, a major disadvantage of hot oil being its tendency to leak at various fittings. Some of the older extruders which are electrically heated do not offer as uniform temperature control as oil heating.

Dry blend extrusions usually require finer mesh screens than is characteristic of extrusions using granular or pelletized resin. The finer the screen packing in the extruder, the greater is the degree of "hold back" of the resin. A number of factors contribute to the back pressure of the extruder. As this pressure is increased, the melting zone is moved further back in the extruder and generally better mixing results with subsequent improvement by reduction of both gel and porosity. The breaker plate, screen sizes, particular extrusion die, screw design and resin viscosity all contribute to the back pressure. Porosity in vinyl wire coatings can sometimes be reduced by the use of vented extruders. Considerable variation in die design is possible.

5. APPLICATIONS

The major consumption of polymers of vinyl chloride are in wire and cable, molding and extrusion, film and sheeting, flooring, dispersion and coated fabric applications. Among the more prominent applications in the construction industry are wire coating, flooring, paint, various tiles, structural laminates and lighting fixtures. The paint industry consumes polyvinyl acetate in ever increasing amounts.

FILM AND SHEETING

Consumption of calendered vinyl film and sheeting in 1957 is estimated at 121.5 million lb (see Table 1.4).

The growth prospects are considered to be bright. A major factor in this anticipated expanded volume of domestic use is durability and ease of cleaning. These two factors, coupled with a wide range of color possibilities, enhance the use of vinyls in the home furnishings market. Leather-like finishes have the greatest sale, followed by textured effects. Both supported and unsupported sheeting are expected to exhibit good growth, while nylon-backed vinyls are gaining in popularity with high-quality furniture manufacturers. Dinette furniture, lounge sofas, chairs and television cabinets are major outlets for vinyl film and sheeting in the home.

Increased applications have been made for vinyl laminated

to foam materials. The automotive industry continues to be a large outlet for vinyl latex for bonding nonwoven fibers, which in turn have an exterior of a vinyl coating. The old application of vinyl resins in shower curtains continues to hold its own having some 70% or more of the total volume. Vinyl sheeting in inflatables is increasing, and it is reported that sales of vinyl swimming pools in the east in 1957 were double the sales of 1956.

Although leather-like vinyls find the greatest application in home furniture, textured effects which resemble soft goods are expected to make inroads on the "leathers." Among new items gaining in popularity are vinyl upholstered beds. The combination of sheeting and woven fabrics seems to have the greatest possibility of accelerated sale for living room furniture. In deep-spring furniture vinyl supported material is preferred to unsupported. In upholstered furniture the resin applications for the most part fall in the mid-price range. There is a sharp disagreement among furniture manufacturers whether the primary sale of vinyl furniture will continue to lie in the field resembling leather or whether textured plastic upholstery will eventually be superior in the consumer market.

Vinyl rainwear can be made more comfortable by the incorporation of many small vents which allow the film to "breathe." The relatively low moisture vapor transmission rate of vinyl film is overcome by breather holes and the film still remains water-repellent. Comfort to the wearer is gained by an increase in the moisture vapor transmission rate of approximately 700% over continuous plastic film. It is expected that the same type of vented vinyl film will be applicable in the manufacture of mattress and pillow covers, aprons, furniture and cushion covers and baby wear. Film and sheeting can be made for specialty purposes by proper compounding and formulation. Such vinyl materials as boilable and soap-resistant films, as well as plastic film which will give good service at low temperatures, are obtained by modification of formulation.

Some of the vinyl film usage in the home is in shower curtains, aprons, furniture covers, kitchen bowl covers, mattress and pillow covers, blanket and clothing bags, basket liners, draperies and ruffling, card table covers and shelf lining. Major industrial uses of film and sheeting are automotive seat covers and protectors, tarpaulins, electrical and decorative tapes, various insulation materials and agricultural. Clothing applications and accessories of film are baby pants and clothing lining, bathinettes and various outerwear including jackets and raincoats. Traveling bags, bathing suit and beach bags also account for volume fabrication. Miscellaneous film applications are tobacco pouches, swimming pools, inflatable toys and balls and embossed movie screens.

Vinyl Films in Agriculture

Applications of vinyl and other plastic films in agriculture have been in vogue since about 1950. The use of vinyls for agricultural purposes is still not large, but some believe this will be an outlet of great volume in a few years. Whether this enthusiastic view is fulfilled is difficult to predict. Minor applications of vinyl film have been such relatively small applications as air layering for plant propagation. The low water vapor transmission rate of the film has led to use as wrapping for cuttings and small plants which are shipped in wet moss. Vinyl silos have been larger outlets for film and sheeting. It has been reported that covering of trenches filled with silage gives excellent preservation from rain and spoilage at a very low storage cost. Polyethylene and vinyl film compete for a section of the agricultural outlet. For mulching and row covers polyethylene (particularly black) has a decided edge over plasticized vinyls.

It is in dispute whether silos of vinyl or polyethylene are the more serviceable. Contradictory statements are made in this regard. However, it has been demonstrated vinyl film has higher tear resistance. Vinyl tarpaulins are used to cover haymows. Massive volume use of polyvinyl chloride in the manufacture of low-cost silos is expected by some observers. These silos are merely various size applications of film which are open end sleeves in which silage can be stored. It is reported that spoilage of such animal feed is quite low in

(Courtesy Bakelite Company)

Figure 5.1. Vinyl plastic bag silo.

these containers. The high strength and low weight of film and sheeting add to the popularity of the item for silo covers. It is believed that the plasticized material has entirely adequate low temperature performance and weather resistance. The high chemical resistance of PVC offers the maximum of protection against lactic acid, formed as a product of fermentation of the silage. Vinyl film permits the passage of carbon dioxide evolved during fermentation, while keeping water and excessive air away from the silage. Silo covers may be used for trench silos or those entirely above ground level. A form of fencing may be used for the latter type and the silage added in successive tiers. If this method of silo use ever becomes universal in its appeal, it will most certainly involve a major sale of PVC for such an application.

Vinyl-nylon sheet is used as tarpaulins by the agricultural, transportation and construction industries. The material is capable of being electronically welded, and is of high strength and waterproofness. The use of covers for athletic fields is fostered by the relatively light weight of heavy duty material. Rigid vinyl sheeting has been used for lining walls of semi-permanent silos.

Reservoirs

An application of film with considerable promise is a means for controlling seepage losses in farm reservoirs. An excellent article has been published by Lauritzen and co-workers at Utah State Agricultural College. This work has been done in cooperation with the United States Department of Agriculture.

The studies of Lauritzen involve polyethylene and vinyl resins and were made of biological deterioration, weathering, root and sprout penetration, rupture under hydrostatic heads, mechanical damage, cushioning effect of water, stable slopes for cover material and seepage from the lined reservoirs. Various thicknesses of polyethylene, both clear and black, and several thicknesses of vinyl film containing a number of different plasticizers were studied. It was found that vinyls deteriorated more rapidly than polyethylene when exposed to actinic radiation. Various roots penetrated both films and it was not clearly defined which was preferable. Rupture tests of both four and eight mil vinyl film were considered to be satisfactory when tested by a hydrostatic head of 30 psi for a period a week.

Mechanical damage to polyethylene was much more severe than to vinyls when tested in covering operations by throwing gravel upon specimens placed on the bottom of a reservoir.

This damage is considered to be a highly important factor in effective field installation of plastic films. It was found that covering operation difficulties of the film were minimized by the cushioning effect of water. Therefore, covering with gravel should be considered with the reservoir full of water. Better outdoor durability is provided with opaque or practically opaque film than with clear material.

(Courtesy Utah State University,
U. S. Department of Agriculture)

Figure 5.2. Installation of 120' x 90' PVC liner for farm pond.

A vinyl lining for a reservoir at Emery, Utah, used a liner 90 × 120 ft. The liner was pulled into place in a few minutes and anchored by burying in a trench along the top edge of the reservoir slope. Cover was provided by several inches of clay loam in 2 to 3 in. of gravel. Prior to using the vinyl liner, this reservoir had to be filled every week or ten days. Accurate measurements of water loss are not available, but indications are that the lining is effective in controlling losses.

Both polyethylene and vinyl films offered certain advantages in the above test work. The abrasion resistance of vinyl is better than polyethylene, while sunlight resistance of black polyethylene was better than vinyl. Fabrication of polyethylene was considered to be much more of a problem than with vinyl liners as it was difficult to get a good bond at the seam in thicker polyethylene film. Excellent bonds were obtained with heat-sealed vinyls. Polyethylene also showed failure along folds of the film, as was noted in some types of vinyl films. Cost comparisons were approximately 24 cents per sq yd for 8 mil polyethylene, while vinyl in similar thickness was 32 cents.

It is estimated that losses due to seepage in stock watering ponds are as great as 50%. Vinyl linings have reduced such water losses to evaporation.

Vinyl sheeting has been used for lining concrete cooling tanks to eliminate water seepage through the concrete wall. Watertight vinyl liners are also used in home swimming pools, the liner being applied over the concrete bottom and sides, or in some cases used in open pits with the liner placed against the bare earth in a manner somewhat similar to that used for lining agriculture ponds.

Contradictions are found as to the potential of vinyl sheeting in preventing water loss in irrigation ditches. It is possible that this is a potentially great volume application of both polyethylene and PVC. However, Lauritzen, writing in the 1955 "Year Book of Agriculture" on the subject of "Water," has this to say under the subject of ways to control water losses from seepage:

"Preliminary investigations of plastic film and synthetic rubber sheeting for use as exposed liners have not been entirely promising. It is almost impossible to install these thin membranes in a canal without some wrinkling which is objectionable. Their thinness makes them subject to damage by livestock, farm equipment and other hazards to which canal linings are subjected. Those objections are eliminated when the materials are used as buried linings. The thin linings have the characteristics of other types of buried linings."

It is interesting to report the observations of the same author, who comments that the plastic materials due to their lightness in weight, make for easier installation. Wrinkles will not impair the effectiveness of the membrane as a barrier against percolating water and, as it is buried, will not modify the surface characteristics of the lining. It is stated that the cost of a 3-in. unreenforced concrete canal lining including installation of subgrade is about $3.00 a sq yd. Buried asphalt membrane linings cost about $1.00 per sq yd, and membrane linings of polyvinyl chloride film may cost a little less.

Vinyl Laminates

Naugatuck Chemical has made significant contribution to the art of vinyl-metal laminates. The processes involved in the preparation of good vinyl-metal laminates are a thorough cleaning of the metal followed by application of the adhesive, evaporation of the solvent, reactivation of the adhesive tack and finally application of the vinyl itself. Washing of the metal by alkali or acid media is followed by a water rinse to remove the cleaning solution completely. The metal is then coated by any of several materials to give better adhesion. A commonly used coating is iron phosphate, followed by a hot water rinse and finally a hot rinse with dilute chromic acid.

Knowledge of this particular lamination technique has been made public by Arvin Industries, who have found that any alkali present on the metal surface at the time of adhesive application lessens the bond strength. After the metal is thoroughly dried, it is conveyed to a roller coater and the adhesive applied. Vinyl acetate based adhesives are used by some industries. Some users of the adhesive technique state that the adhesive thickness must be uniform and approximately 0.5 mil, as material much thinner or thicker gives decreased bond strength.

Another problem which faces this industry is to find adhesives which may be reactivated well below their decomposition temperature, the latter generally being in the vicinity of 400°F. The metal containing the adhesive is passed through a heated zone to remove all residual solvent and then the adhesive reactivated by heat. Roll pressure applies the vinyl sheeting to the metal surface. It has been found that in some cases a pressure of 50 psi is satisfactory for optimum bonding conditions.

Highly plasticized stock is generally unsatisfactory, as excessive migration occurs and gives poor strength of the bond. It is believed that completely unplasticized vinyl sheeting has not been used to the present, and a lightly plasticized resin is the most satisfactory. Water sprays are sometimes used to cool the laminate prior to storing. The laminate may be styled by a variety of patterns and designs. The lamination technique has been applied using a number of different metals because of decorative value, wear and abrasion resistance, corrosion resistance and sound deadening qualities of the construction.

A vinyl steel laminate has been developed by John Summers & Sons in Britain. The material is described as the first continuous strip mill, cold reduced steel-vinyl laminate to be produced. A PVC coating of 14 mils is bonded to a treated surface of the steel using a synthetic rubber adhesive. This material is reputedly comparable in price with high quality enamel finish and offers an added advantage as the vinyl coating follows the contours of the steel quite closely. This application is expected to be used for cabinets, wall panels and office furniture.

Naugatuck's "Marvibond" process consists of sheet metal to which vinyl film is firmly laminated to both sides of the metal. Excellent chemical and corrosion resistance are provided and the laminate can be stamped into various structural designs or embossed with decorated patterns. Cold-rolled sheet steel of 18 to 34 gauge has been used, although these thicknesses may be increased or decreased as desired. Aluminum, magnesium, brass and copper can also replace steel with equal facility. Films have been applied ranging from 2 to 20 mils. Film of all colors is processed but, as would be expected, the choice of pigment used affects various properties of the laminate. A wide range of hardness, elongation and general properties of the film coatings can be varied to meet special requirements. PVC most often employed is of a high molecular weight to give maximum chemical resistance and heat stability. These latter properties are significantly superior to vinyl copolymer resins applied in solution. The "Marvibond" process cannot use solution resins either practically or economically because of marked webbing tendencies when solid concentrations greater than 10% are used, and because of the high cost of solvents. An economy of this process is the absence of expensive ketone or ester solvents, which generally are used in solution grade resins to the extent of 40% or more. The cost of these laminates is comparable to lacquered thin surfaces and lower in cost than lacquered thick films. The chemical, water and humidity resistant laminate is dimensionally stable below 250°F.

Good abrasion resistance, electrical properties, non-combustibility and wide color possibilities all enhance the product appeal. These materials have been used in fabrication of chemical tanks, industrial roofing, automobile fenders and bodies, ventilating ducts, air washing systems, chemical conduit pipe and troughs, and back-up plates in switch boxes. Further outlets are provided in building sidings, table tops, hospital equipment, machine housings and lawn and office furniture. Most of the above applications are satisfactory when 8 mil PVC film is laminated although heavier gauge vinyls are often used when embossing is required.

Vinyl-metal laminates have the advantages of providing a continuous method for coating metal, a finish of excellent durability, a wide variety of style and design, a material which will not support combustion, and which possesses good sound-deadening properties, and a product capable of being worked by a number of metal-working techniques such as deep-drawing, crimping, stamping, punching, shearing and reverse-bending without rupture of the film. This technique does have a disadvantage of not permitting spot welding, and does not provide for covering of the metal edges which is necessary where severe exposure conditions will be encountered. The service temperature limitations are those normally dictated by vinyl film or sheeting. The inability to reprocess scrap readily to salvage the metal makes an efficient lamination operation necessary.

Laminates as well as unsupported film are finding a considerably broader scope in agriculture; they are employed as row covers, silos, as ensilage protectors and as linings for irrigation ditches and storage ponds.

O'Sullivan Rubber Corporation has developed a laminate using rigid or semi-rigid sheeting onto adhesive coated metal sheets. The laminate is made by a rolling technique under the application of heat. This lamination has found application in the manufacture of television cabinets. Vinyl-metal laminates in the preparation of "Samsonite" luggage use substantial amounts of the resin. Lamination of vinyl sheeting to itself and which sandwiches glass or metals has application in the manufacture of jewelry, handbags and novelty wear. The laminate may consist of two vinyl sheetings or a third sheet. Where three sheets are used, the second laminate is usually printed on a clear sheet and this in turn laminated to a third overlay sheet. Outerwear which resembles leather is a large application of laminated vinyl sheeting to cloth. The material has excellent flexibility and is windproof and water-proof. Grain patterns resembling various leathers are readily accomplished.

Another application of vinyls is in wall covering, although this is not as yet a large-volume application. One major manufacturer believes that volume outlets of PVC will lie in a special process by which vinyl film of 4 to 12 mil gauge is laminated to a cotton fabric. This lamination of the vinyl to the scrim is done by an adhesive process. The laminate is adhered to any type of wall including steel and glass by a special paste. The manufacturers of wall paper coverings believe that this type of vinyl application, which will provide excellent wear and mar resistance, will regain the market which their business has lost to the emulsion paints. A leading manufacturer of this type of wall covering is Velveray Corporation.

Laminates of vinyl film, in particular a vinyl-nylon laminate, have great strength and are considerably lighter than the old canvas coverings. An excellent material is provided by a covering consisting of two pieces of vinyl film sandwiching a nylon net. Such a covering is as much as one-third lighter than canvas and has excellent applications for massive coverings of athletic fields, etc.

Cast Vinyl Film

The casting of vinyl resin on paper is not a new technique, having been known since about 1945, and is predicted by some to be on the verge of large-volume production. This casting process can be used not only for coating of various papers and fabrics, but also as a method of stripping the vinyl from the carrier as a means of preparing thin films. This method may some day compete with calendered film, and some authorities assert that this method is far more service-able than the preparation of thin gauge film by blown extrusion. It is believed that coating rates using plastisol resins have been obtained as high as 400 ft per min.

Vinyl film cast on a paper carrier does not block or stick and can be stored for an indefinite period of time prior to stripping off the coating. Plastisol application permits the paper carrier to be reused a number of times after the plastic is stripped off. If the paper carrier is first embossed, a light pattern may be imparted to the resin. The surface of the paper carrier determines whether the film finish is dull or has a high luster. Plastisol casting technique on paper can provide film as thin as produced by the blown extrusion technique. Considerable variation can be made in the composition of the plastisol or organosol involved in this technique, and such variations markedly affect the release rate of the film. Little is known about the fusion temperature of the varied materials, but it is likely that this temperature may be as high as 450°F.

Cast film is also made by a spreading or casting of a vinyl chloride-vinyl acetate resin in solution on a stainless steel belt. As this belt is passed through an oven, the volatile solvent is removed. The thickness of the film is controlled by variations in the speed of the belt as the solution is cast upon it. Film so obtained is characterized by good clarity, high tear strength and comparative freedom from strains. The films also have a relatively high degree of imperviousness to moisture vapor and common gases. The casting technique of the vinyl chloride-acetate copolymer can be utilized to produce both plasticized and unplasticized films of 1-10 mils in thickness. The product manufactured by Bakelite as "Krene" is obtainable in widths up to 48 inches and can be readily heat-sealed.

Rigid film has application as overlays and skin-packaging in which the film is formed tightly over and around items for display purposes. The preferred method of sealing cast vinyl film is by heat-sealing techniques, although sewing operations and adhesives are also employed. The problem of printing is comparable to that of calendered film as the same inks are used. Among major applications of plasticized film are use in garment bags, notions, seat covers, foil and paper laminates, storm windows, and food packaging. The generally good weathering properties permit use as tractor cab housing and window glazing.

Emulsion polymer can be directly applied in the form of a latex for the preparation of sheets and various coatings.

(Courtesy Bakelite Company)

Figure 5.3. Vinyl "bubble" holds argon gas for inert welding of titanium.

This technique is still relatively new, but it does offer attractive advantages in that costly spray drying is avoided and economy is effected by fabric coating and dip-coating processes. The latex is thickened by the use of materials such as carboxymethyl cellulose and certain salts. Films are prepared from plasticized latexes by heating the film at 300°F.

A unique application of cast vinyl film by Pratt and Whitney Aircraft involves film shaped in the form of a tent for use in welding of titanium metal used in jet engine parts. The low gas transmission rate of cast film permits the tent to be swept clean using argon gas to remove air of the atmosphere. The titanium welding can then be made without outside contamination.

Printing on Vinyl

In addition to constantly new uses for film and sheeting it is believed that prospect of a substantial growth pattern for these materials lies in the advanced styling of today's products. Much of the increased volume of film and sheeting is due to fabricators and processors who have developed techniques which yield products of beautiful and stylized printing and embossing.

Vinyl film and sheeting may be printed by four processes. These methods are gravure, surface, screen and embossing, and valley printing. These and new techniques are unquestionably responsible for much of the success of the industry. The highly stylized fabrics of today represent a substantial improvement over the plain, solid-colored film and sheeting of the past. Many improvements in the industry now permit the long wear and practicability of the vinyls to be combined with the beauty of woven textiles.

Decorated vinyl film for drapes, curtains, table cloths, rainwear and many other products is often printed by the gravure process. This consists of the deposition of an ink on the film surface from the recesses or "cups" of a cylindrical engraving. The desired pattern is etched into the metal. Some fine engravings have as many as 200 cups per inch. These gravure machines are designed so that printing may involve one to six colors. The tiny cups are filled with color, the excess removed by a doctor blade, and the ink then brought into contact with the film and transferred to it. The printing roll is resupplied with ink by rotation toward the color box. These inks are pigments which are dispersed in various resins which give good adhesion to the vinyl to be printed and are used in conjunction with rapid-drying solvents. Considerable variation in color and shade are obtained by varying the depth of the engraving, which in turn regulates the thickness of the deposited ink. The gravure process permits excellent color patterns and uniformity at high production speeds.

Surface printing permits three-dimensional effects and the use of as many as twelve colors. This technique differs from the gravure process in that the engravings are from a pattern which is raised above the roll and not recessed. The printing costs by surface and gravure methods are high and cannot be utilized except in large production orders. Screen printing, which in effect is a form of stencil, is cheaper and can be used for smaller volume production. Valley printing, which is used to some extent on film and to a larger extent for sheeting, is exhibiting increasing promise. This method permits either light or deep embossing and a wide range of patterns. This method permits simultaneous coloring and embossing, and gains its name "valley" as the inks are delivered to the design on an embossing role into the valley of the material as it is being embossed.

Plastisol ink containing vinyl resins offer some liabilities, as the accompanying solvents present fire hazards, and the fusion temperature can distort the embossed pattern. These objections have resulted in the development of aqueous printing inks which consist of dispersions of resins and pigments.

These materials have found application in gravure and valley printing. Another advantage of the aqueous systems is that the absence of organic solvent eliminates solvent attack of the rubber printing rolls. The pigments used in vinyl printing must have a high resistance to bleeding, and the pigment must therefore be resistant to the plasticizer used in the film or sheeting or the solvent used in conjunction with the ink. Pigments also must have a high degree of light resistance and in certain applications be resistant to extraction by soapy water, resist mild acids and alkalies and not stain due to contact with foods.

MISCELLANEOUS

Greater accuracy in measuring film thickness has been a needed development. The National Physical Laboratory in England has recently developed pneumatic equipment which can be used with thin, soft film. This apparatus is capable of measurement without compression of the material to an accuracy of $\pm$ 20 microinches while measuring film of thickness from 0.001 to 0.02 inch.

The effect on many plastics when exposed to atomic attack has been studied by the U. S. Government. A report was presented by the S.P.I. in 1957 which gave some results of the tests at Yucca Flats, Nevada. Final results of these tests have not been made public except those data presented by the S.P.I. It was reported by the S.P.I. that both vinyl and saran experienced extensive melting under the test conditions. Some vinyl sheeting, both plasticized and rigid, was essentially undamaged in certain tests, but at this time the practicability of vinyls used as protection against atomic blasts is uncertain. Brookhaven National Laboratories process radioisotopes in rooms which have been sprayed with strippable vinyls; after becoming radioactive the film is stripped from the walls and destroyed.

Blown Extrusion of Film

Little technical data have been released which describe the details of vinyl blown extrusion. This is done by Clopay Corporation and Goodyear Tire & Rubber. Experimental work suggests that extrusion using a circular die is accomplished at temperatures between 375°F. and possibly as high as 450°F. One mil film was priced in 1957 at 79 cents per lb, which gives an approximate yield of 21,500 sq in. Film is obtainable in roll form up to 38 in. wide. The film is recommended for machine and hand packaging, low-temperature applications and for the manufacture of bags and pouches. At the present time the production of vinyl film of good quality and close tolerance as thin as 1 mil is not made in the United States for commercial sale using calendering operations. It is reported that calenders are available in Germany which can make good quality 1 mil film. Blown extrusion, however, is still believed to be the only commercial method in the United States for the preparation of these thin films. Fisheyes continue to be a problem with blown extrusion operations. It appears that high processing temperatures are necessary to develop maximum tear strength. The film can be prepared using 30 parts or more dioctyl phthalate to 100 parts of resin and stabilized by the usual 2 part level of heat stabilizers. Lubricants are necessary in quantities higher than usual in extrusion operations and may include various stearates, oils and waxes in concentrations of as high as 1-2 parts.

The gauge of the blown extruded film is controlled by variation in speed of take-up rolls. This material has potential in food packaging provided that the extruded rates are high enough so that the product can be competitive, and that nontoxic stabilizers are incorporated. It may be possible that toxic stabilizers will some day be used even though the material will be used for wrapping foods if it can be demonstrated to the Government authorities that extraction of the toxic material is zero.

Blown extruded thin-walled PVC film may use either a dry blend or granules, which are plasticized or rigid, and extruded preferably using a straight die. The extrusion rates of such film are relatively low although films are prepared of good quality of a thickness of approximately ½ to 5 mils.

(Courtesy The B. F. Goodrich Company)

Figure 5.4. Flame-resistant vinyl film provides fire protection for 34 acre Chrysler roof.

Uses

Goodrich has supplied a fire-retardant roofing which consists of a vinyl barrier and a nonflammable adhesive. This construction was used to cover the entire 34-acre roof of a new Chrysler plant at Twinsburg, Ohio. The roofing was finished by a sixty-man crew in less than six months. The construction using vinyl film eliminates asphalt materials from between roof, deck and insulation, which during fire evolve combustible gases.

Firestone Plastics Company supplies a specially formulated vinyl film for application in wall coverings. The film is fused to a fabric backing and printed to afford long life and washability. Unsupported film using pressure sensitive tape backing permits adhesion to walls and furniture.

Adhesive decals of vinyl are for application to furniture and walls. The vinyl is provided with an adhesive which is protected by paper which, when peeled off, permits direct application of the decal.

The need for protective closures of vinyl has prompted attention by a number of manufacturers to the use of zippers. FlexiGrip, Incorporated, has developed both vinyl and polyethylene runners by an extrusion technique to which are applied conventional metal slides for opening and closing. The use of such zippers in vinyl film and sheeting permits many applications for sealing clothing which will be dust- and moth-proof and an attractive application for rubber footwear. It is expected that military applications of vinyl-zippered composition will be developed for shielding mechanical parts and motors from weather and corrosion and for enclosing large missiles such as the "Corporal." Apparatus used for measuring radiation intensity can be protected by disposable vinyl coverings.

United Shoe Machinery Corporation has developed a vinyl insole using a layer of porous vinyl laminated between layers of a latex impregnated backing. Superior wearing qualities and good comfort are reported. Thin vinyl tapes with pressure sensitive adhesives serve as printed instruction labels and wiring diagrams for various instruments.

Vinyl sheeting is used by various manufacturers for inflatable boats. The sheeting is electronically sealed to provide a rugged material which is not easily punctured.

Columbus Coated Fabrics has recently introduced in their "Wall-Tex" line, vinyl shower sets and vinyl coated cotton of a high degree of color matching. The cloth coatings are made of a solution application covered by a vinyl film over the printed material. This permits a permanent designed fabric.

PVC barges may soon be fabricated of sheeting possibly of a reinforced nature. This will facilitate many chemicals to be cheaply shipped via water. A number of such barges may be towed by a single tug and possibly reused or scrapped as the economy will dictate. Germany is the first country to investigate such vinyl tubes for waterway shipping.

VINYL FOAMS

Rubber foams are encountering competition from a number of plastic foam materials, and it is evident that the future of these materials is uncertain. Major plastic foam materials are vinyl, styrene and urethane, although the phenolics, silicones, cellulose acetate, polyethylene and a styrene-butadiene-methacrylic acid terpolymer all may challenge.

It is risky to predict the market for resilient foams by 1960. Estimates have been made that the growing foam market will exceed 500 million lb of the products by 1960. Similar estimates predict that foam latex by 1960 will exceed 300 million lb; vinyl foam production will be in the order of 150 million lb and urethane foam approximately 125 million. These estimates appear optimistic. It is also difficult to predict competitive costs of vinyl versus latex and urethane foams. At this writing the urethane foams can be produced with the lowest density, followed by vinyl foams and with latex foam the most dense. It is reported that good quality vinyl foam has been prepared experimentally with a density of 3-4 lb versus the usual 6 pound density of today's market. If this is realized coupled with lower raw material costs, vinyl foam will be an even greater challenger to urethane foam, which at present has approximately one-half the density of the vinyl on a volume basis. It is generally believed that the simplicity of vinyl and urethane foam preparation permits substantially lower capital investment costs than is possible with foamed latex.

Certainly the higher chemical, solvent, and oil resistance are advantages of vinyl and polyurethane foams over latex. Urethane foams are of great interest because of their low density of 2-3 lb/cu ft. It is possible that if a 3-4 lb/cu ft density of vinyl foams is realized, this will more than offset the reduction in the cost of polyurethanes due to use of 25 cent a pound polyether glycols instead of 50 cents a pound polyesters.

Vinyl foams are prepared from plastisol resin. The two major methods to form the required cellular structure are by mechanical means and the incorporation of chemical blowing agents.

It is possible to widely vary the character of the foam cell structure and composition by formulation and process variations. The load-carrying ability can be adjusted to specific requirements by such formulation, which can result in considerable changes in the density. Vinyl foams are relatively insensitive to oxidation and hardening, and these qualities are an advantage over latex materials. Cored foams have been made in thicknesses up to 6 inches and sheet stock as wide as 36 in. in a 2½-in. thick slab. It is suspected that sheet 72 in. wide and up to 6 in. thick is currently available. Variations in density from perhaps 4-30 lb/cu ft can be made. Application in crash pads require a "dead" material with low rebound, which is readily accomplished in vinyl foams and not obtainable in latex. It is also possible to manufacture a resilient foam with high rebound. The good aging qualities of vinyl products generally are also characteristic of the foams. Resistance of vinyl foam to hydrolysis and mildew are also important factors. The material can be readily die cut to desired shape and as thin as $\frac{1}{16}$ in. Material may be cast in open or closed molds with or without coring to form a resilient cushion. Intricate shapes are possible by specialized molding techniques.

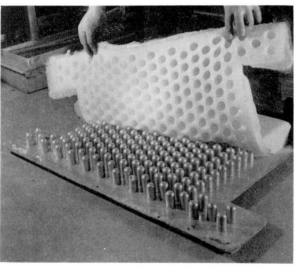

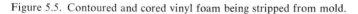

Figure 5.5. Contoured and cored vinyl foam being stripped from mold.

Vinyl foams which are manufactured by incorporation of a chemical additive or "blowing agent" require this additive to have a decomposition temperature below the gel temperature of the resin. Among the more popular blowing agents are BL-353 made by duPont and "Celogen" by Naugatuck Chemical. These agents utilize the evolution of nitrogen to produce cellular structure.

All vinyl foams require heating in their curing operations. Briefly, closed cell vinyl foams are made by dispersing the blowing agent in a plastisol resin which is fused in closed molds under pressures which sometime exceed 2,000 psi. As differentiated from unicellular PVC, the plastisol can be fused at atmospheric pressure by the use of an inert gas under initial pressure and then cured thermally in a molded slab or sheet. The latter method is known as the Elastomer Process.

Preparation of Vinyl Foams: Chemical Blowing Agents

A major method of preparation of vinyl foams is by intro-duction of organic blowing agents which release nitrogen upon decomposition. The material manufactured by duPont under the trade name "BL-353" is chemically N,N^1-dimethyl-N,N^1-dinitrosoterephthalamide. It is important that the blow-ing agent decompose completely at temperatures lower than the temperature required to gel the plastisol, i.e., in excess of 120°C. A firm temperature specification cannot be stated, as the quantity and types of plasticizers also have a contribut-ing influence on gelation temperature. Successful decomposi-tion of the organic chemical blowing agent and foaming of the plastisol is accomplished by conduction heating and also by dielectric methods.

Emulsion grade PVC only is used as the resin component. Some success in the preparation of stable foams has been realized using vinyl chloride-vinyl acetate copolymers as well as copolymers of vinyl chloride and vinylidene chloride. Foaming of these latter two copolymer compositions is not believed to be commercial at this time as added difficulties occur when these polymer systems are used.

The choice of plasticizer to use with PVC in the prepara-tion of flexible foams is highly important. Perhaps of major consideration is the selection of plasticizers with low solvating action toward the resin, as the viscosity of the plastisol must be carefully regulated. It has been observed that dispersion resins which contain excessive amounts of emulsifier cause the resulting foam to be of poor quality. The importance of the effect of residual water accompanying the PVC is disputed by various fabricators, although little dispute is found among them in regard to the importance of using resin of low solvating power. The majority opinion is that moisture associated with the PVC resin must be lower than $\frac{1}{10}$ of a percent in order to avoid difficulties in formulation.

Naugatuck Chemical's "Celogen" is chemically p,p'-oxy-bis-(benzene sulfonyl hydrazide) and is a valuable blowing agent. The chemical blowing agents under proper conditions can be used to produce both open and closed cell types of wide density range. The types and amounts of plasticizers employed have a marked effect on the physical properties of the finished foam as well as causing variations in the volume of the foam. Mixed plasticizers, both monomeric and polymeric in nature, are frequently employed.

So many variations in plasticizer volume and identity can be made that it is impossible to give a fixed formulation until the end use is known. However, a generalization is that an often used plasticizer volume is 100 parts to 100 parts of PVC. Varying amounts of blowing agent are used at a level of 5 parts and much greater. The stabilizers often employed are liquid barium-cadmium in conjunction with liquid epoxy in a total charge of the order of 5 parts. Various fillers may be used.

Chemical blowing agents such as "BL-353" must be handled with caution as the material is a weak explosive, sensitive to impact and friction, and in the presence of strong alkalies decomposes to the toxic and explosive gas diazomethane.

Vinyl foams can be made under pressure or at atmospheric pressure. It is of value to mix the components thoroughly by high shear, using a paint mill or similar apparatus. The blowing agent may be dispersed in the plasticizers for use as a masterbatch. The total cycle for expansion and fusion may require as long as an hour or substantially less, as such factors as the amount and composition of the charge have important roles.

Inorganic foaming agents have also been tried but to date do not have the potential of organic blowing agents. Alkali metal bicarbonates have been used in attempts to make plastic foam of vinylidene chloride copolymers.

Mechanically blown vinyl foam can be made by application of the Elastomer Process, described in U. S. Patent 2,666,036. In this process the plastisol is charged into a vessel by means of a pump and carbon dioxide is introduced at the pump discharge. The gas is dispersed throughout the container and the plastisol vented onto a casting belt or to a mold by means of a spray. Curing is accomplished by ovens or dielectric methods. This method of mechanical blowing is adaptable for the production of open cell structure.

Vinyl foams for applications in cushioning are used in the form of sheet or slab stock in continuous rolls. Molded cushions and application directly to film or textile can be effected. Application of vinyl foam as a backing for carpets and rugs is made by spraying directly on the fabric and then cured. Seat toppers for railroad cars and furniture are used in sheet form.

The use of foamed vinyl is popular as a lining in jacket wear because of its excellent insulation resistance to wind and cold. Experiments conducted by the Armed Forces reveal that such wear provides lightness and excellent mobility while the jacket wear is entirely adequate after prolonged exposure to extreme cold. The "Cold Bar" suit of the U. S. Army uses foamed vinyl in boots, mittens and the suit itself. Tests reveal that the low moisture absorption of the foam provides an effective barrier against cold even after long immersion in water. Similar insulation against cold has found application in providing a lining around cabs of army vehicles in Arctic regions.

Use of the foam as a thermal insulation barrier is also applicable for lining cold storage cabinets, refrigerated vehicles, various shipping containers, and gasket material for refrigerator doors. Gaskets to be used on the back of refrigerators adequately seal the evaporator and yet permit ready access for servicing. Kelvinator applies a vinyl plastisol to a shallow groove around the edge of a metal panel which is later cured at a temperature of 350°F. The plastic gasket has been effective in place of costlier and less serviceable mastic tapes.

The capital investment required to manufacture vinyl foam in 1957 was believed to be as low as 15-20% of that for latex foams.

Vinyl foam has a number of applications which have resulted from its properties of resiliency, flexibility, solvent and chemical resistance, flame resistance and resistance to abrasion, tearing, moisture and aging. The cushioning field is a potential major outlet in public transportation. Breathing is afforded by interconnecting cells. Excellent dimensional stability is provided by vinyl foams and shrinkage is negligible. Although vinyl foams have so far found little volume consumption in seating applications, it is quite possible that this generally good quality will ultimately permit it to compete with foam rubber. The New York City Transit Authority has installed vinyl foam in some new subway cars. Some of the many applications of vinyl foam are in mattresses, automotive crash padding, seating, upholstery and paneling for the automotive industry, pillows, upholstery, wall and furniture coverings in various laminations and innersoles. Other uses are in carpet backing, sponges for cleaning purposes, various furniture components, industrial shock mountings, gaskets, belts, toys and outersoles.

Automobile arm rests can be made in a unique process in which the mounting plate of the article is an insert in the mold whose inner wall is embossed to reproduce an outer surface design on the vinyl foam which fills the mold. Although the use of vinyl foam in the automotive industry, as well as in all other industries, is quite small, it is expected to grow. Other automotive applications in 1957 were certain padding applications, automotive door and roof linings, sun visors and taxi jump seats. Vinyl cushions are still a small operation but have good prospects of growth. A relatively new application attractive to furniture and automotive manufacturers consists of sandwiching vinyl foam between a fabric backing and a vinyl skin. Unicellular vinyl sponge is used in flotation equipment such as life jackets and various floats, insulation and linings for outerwear.

A significant advantage of vinyl foam over its competition is its ease of electronic sealing. Today's market in furniture upholstery has realized a particular advantage due to the ease of vinyl heat-sealing. Polyurethane foam based on polyesters is quite poor in this regard. Vinyl foam will weld to itself as well as vinyl film and sheeting or supported vinyl fabrics.

It is conceivable that a greatly accelerated sale of vinyl foam would be realized if the stiffness imparted by low temperatures and the decreased load-carrying ability at high temperatures could be eliminated. Vinyl foam is quite definitely in its infancy and it is believed that the total volume usage in 1958 will not exceed 15 million lb.

Polyvinyl formal can also be expanded by nonchemical methods to produce open cell foam. This involves mechanical aeration of a solution of polyvinyl alcohol which contains formaldehyde and an acid, usually sulfuric.

Rigid polystyrene is the major material used in the preparation of these types of plastic foams. Polyurethanes and rigid vinyls are as yet of lesser importance. Rigid vinyl foams have growth possibilities in production of flotation equipment due to high physical strength and non-flame supporting characteristics. The long life and resistance to sea water make rigid vinyl foams particularly adaptable for fish net floats.

POLYVINYL ALCOHOL

PVA is a versatile material. It is a chemical intermediate in the manufacture of polyvinyl butyral, which has its major outlet as a flexible film interlayer that gives safety glass its nonshattering quality. A broad general industrial use of PVA is in adhesives and binders, plastics, film, paper, textile sizings, ceramics, emulsifying and thickening agents, and in temporary protective coatings.

The most important single use of PVA as such is as an emulsifying agent in the preparation of stable, high solids emulsions of polyvinyl acetate. This generally involves the use of medium viscosity, completely hydrolyzed material.

Emulsions are often adversely affected by acidic conditions, particularly when anionic-type emulsifiers are employed. It would be expected that nonionic-type emulsifiers would be the least affected by extreme conditions of high or low pH. DuPont reports that high and medium viscosity 76-79% hydrolyzed polyvinyl acetate is outstanding in producing stable emulsions under acidic conditions. Medium viscosity, similarly hydrolyzed polyvinyl acetate allows relatively stable emulsions at a pH of 2, and high viscosity polymer hydrolyzed to the same extent is effective at a pH of 3 and higher. Other polyvinyl alcohols do not give stable emulsions until a pH of at least 5.5 is obtained. Thus, a low viscosity, 86-89% hydrolyzed polymer and a high viscosity, completely hydro-lyzed polyvinyl acetate produce emulsions which are much more stable at pH 7 or 12.5 than at pH 5.5. Such agents as methylcellulose, glue and natural gums which might be ex-pected to give stable emulsions at low pH do not do so. Anionic agents represented by sodium dodecyl sulfate are ineffective at low pH.

Solutions of PVA frequently foam and even after reduc-tion of agitation this foaming problem can be acute. Octyl alcohol and DC Anti-foam made by Dow-Corning are effective when used to the extent of about 0.1%.

In applications as a binder PVA is quite efficient with a wide number of materials, including clay, ceramics, textile fibers and many fillers. High-viscosity grades find an additional use as binders for nonwoven fabric, while ceramic applications use low viscosity polymer. In powder slip castings and sand molds which later require burning out, a resin of low viscosity and low acetate content performs more satisfactorily. It is observed that adhesion increases as the percent hydrolysis decreases. Therefore, superior adhesion to smooth surfaces is obtained with partially hydrolyzed polymer. The addition of 15% phosphoric acid or 10% urea phosphate based on the weight of "Elvanol" PVA followed by baking for a short time at 100°C. increases adhesion to metal or glass. It is generally accepted that adhesion of PVA to such smooth surfaces is reduced by the incorporation of conventional plasticizers.

Use of polyvinyl alcohol in textile sizing is characterized by imparting high tensile strength, abrasion-resistance, adhesion and flexibility to the material. The solubility of PVA in water greatly simplifies this application. It is important to the textile manufacturer that some agent be used which will give temporary protection to yarn during weaving and knitting operations. The textile size is readily applied by customary methods to the filament and spun yarn, including the new synthetic fibers. In warp sizing the use of polyvinyl alcohol coats the yarn with a continuous film of the water-soluble resin. This tough, colorless, flexible film also penetrates the yarn and generally improves loom performance and quality of the resulting fabric. These features are demonstrated in microphotographs of duPont's "Elvanol" which show good penetration and coating effects on water-absorbent yarns such as cotton, as well as nonabsorbent nylon yarns. The size, ordinarily colorless, has been stained prior to photographing in order to bring out the contrast with the light-colored fiber.

Fibers which readily absorb water can use either partially or completely hydrolyzed polymer. Such is not the case with the newer synthetic fibers, which are much less absorbent. These smooth surface fibers such as nylon and cellulose acetate require partially hydrolyzed PVA. The efficiency of high viscosity material is greater than low viscosity, although in certain cases the desire to make a higher solids concentration in solution necessitates low-viscosity polymer.

Medium to low viscosity partially hydrolyzed polyvinyl alcohol find special application in sizing hydrophobic synthetic filament, as these materials require a size of high adhesion to the yarn. High viscosity, completely hydrolyzed PVA is reported to yield excellent results when used in the preparation of high-tenacity rayon tire cord. Synthetic spun yarn of the acrylic fibers "Dynel," "Acrilan," "Orlon," "Dacron," and nylon require low viscosity, partially hydrolyzed polyvinyl alcohol in conjunction with a modified starch or starch ether. The use of starch is necessary to provide high solids concentration, while PVA improves film strength as well as adhesion to the yarn.

DuPont reports that the product most widely used for sizing nylon hosiery yarn is a water solution of 8.5% low viscosity, partially hydrolyzed polyvinyl alcohol and 1.7% boric acid. The unsized nylon thread travels at mean speed of 2,000 to 3,000 ft per min, and dips into a bath of the size solution. Other textile finishing operations require high viscosity, completely hydrolyzed PVA in supplementing various thermosetting resins. Such resins as melamine-formaldehyde and urea-formaldehyde are used to impart wrinkle and crease-resistance to fabrics. These materials require modification by 5-15% PVA to improve the textile hand and drape. This size is permanent, and the material is fast to washing because polyvinyl alcohol is fixed by chemical reaction with the thermosetting resin.

Paper

Water solutions of PVA are used in the manufacture of many types of paper and impart strength, grease-proofing, special printing qualities and a transparent effect. In producing high-strength paper, high molecular weight, completely hydrolyzed PVA is applied to the paper stock. PVA is used alone or combined with pigments, extenders, and various insolubilizing agents in paper adhesives to give high wet strength, decreased heat susceptibility and improved flexibility. A widely used low-cost adhesive application incorporates PVA with starch and dextrin adhesives to increase both strength and water resistance. If very high wet strengths are required, application of PVA is best made in combination with dimethylol urea. The partially hydrolyzed grades find application in remoistenable adhesives. The added sensitivity of the partially hydrolyzed grades to cold water over the completely hydrolyzed grades makes this application possible. In such uses the tendency for the coated paper to tear, block or stick at high humidities is eliminated.

Glycerin is sometimes employed to increase flexibility of the finished sheet in paper applications. Surface sizing with the resin produces a degree of greaseproofing; however, absolute greaseproofing requires a continuous coating. Most paper sizing applications use high viscosity, completely hydrolyzed polymer. This contributes maximum strength and water resistance and also less tendency to adhere to the calender rolls than with partially hydrolyzed grades. In paper coatings which must remain flexible for long periods of time, it is necessary to plasticize heavily. This requires as much as 50-100% plasticizer based on the dry weight of the polymer when the PVA film is applied to absorbent surfaces. Substantially less plasticizer is sufficient when the application is to nonabsorbent surfaces. In these paper applications conventional sizing and coating equipment can be used to apply the aqueous polyvinyl alcohol solutions.

Use in Polymerizations

Polyvinyl alcohol is used as an emulsifying agent in various vinyl polymerizations. One of the larger outlets of this application is in suspension polymerization of vinyl chloride. Fine particle latices of polystyrene also can be prepared using PVA as the emulsifying agent. Best results are obtained with low viscosity, partially hydrolyzed PVA in emulsion polymerization of styrene systems. High molecular weight, partially hydrolyzed PVA is generally preferred as the suspending agent in the polymerization of vinyl chloride. This is only one of several widely used suspending agents for vinyl chloride, and by no means is PVA universal in this application. PVA can provide a dual function acting in emulsions as both a protective colloid and to some extent as a surface-active agent. Many emulsions prepared using this material have outstanding stability. The requirements of an emulsifier in polymerization have been described in Chapter 4.

PVC latices have been prepared using completely hydrolyzed PVA as an emulsifying agent. In some of these applications medium viscosity PVA allows the preparation of latices with solids concentration as high as 40%-50%. If higher viscosity material is used, the latices which result are of materially lower solids concentration. A general statement in regard to use as an emulsifying agent is that PVA of high viscosity and a low degree of hydrolysis gives the most stable emulsion. In conjunction with polyvinyl acetate emulsions PVA increases viscosity and adhesion. Partially hydrolyzed grades are largely used.

In ceramic applications the polymer has its most important use in the manufacture of stencil screens. This application is also used in photolithographic printing plates. The resin coatings are applied from water solutions which contain ammonium dichromate, and these coatings become water-insoluble when exposed to ultraviolet light. In the manufacture of fine china use of as little as 0.1% PVA based on the dry weight of the clay improves working characteristics. Other similar applications are in anti-abrasion coatings for photographic emulsions, a pigment binder for photographic paper, and in the manufacture of process screens for movie studios. Use in photographic emulsions has replaced gelatin to a minor extent.

Other Applications

Where film clarity is not important, extenders may be used with PVA to lower the cost. Such materials as starch, casein, gelatin, dextrin and urea have been used. None of the above mentioned materials is believed to be completely compatible with PVA. Plasticized PVA can be molded into various articles which exhibit durometer hardness ranging from 10-100. These plastic materials are somewhat rubber-like and are produced in the form of sheeting, tubing, rod and other molded articles. Tubing is used in lubricating equipment in various fuel lines in aircraft and automotive fields. Gaskets are of value where organic solvent resistance is needed. Some use of tubing is due to its resistance to paint and lacquers, refrigerants and various solvents. Tubing is also used in oxygen and compressed air lines.

Other uses of PVA are in printing ink for glass and plastics. Light polarizing film is made from oriented PVA. The polymer is reacted with iodine to form a complex which produces a light-polarizing effect upon orientation. Filaments are produced by spinning aqueous solutions into a coagulating bath of various salts which precipitate the polymer. PVA can be extruded or compression-molded into sheets, tubing, and rods. Volume use may develop for applications which require good nonpolar solvent and gas resistance. Films and coatings of PVA can be made flame-resistant by adding about 10% of ethanolamine ammonium phosphate to the casting or coating solution. In such uses the tendency for the coated paper to tear, block or stick at high humidities is eliminated.

PVA has a modern application in color television picture tubes. The polymer is photosensitized and mixed in water with a color phosphor. This is printed in the desired pattern, in exact register, on the inside face of the tube. This process is repeated three times, once each for the red, green and blue phosphors. Each light-sensitive coating is exposed in turn and that portion of the coating not hardened by the exposures is washed away producing the desired pattern. The pattern is fused by heat, and the remaining PVA burned off so that only the color phosphors remain. In spite of competition from other adhesive binders in the preparation of these TV tubes it is believed that polyvinyl alcohol finds the greater volume usage due to its unique properties. Preference for PVA is undoubtedly due to its requiring no flammable solvents and its easy application and removal. PVA film, which is highly water-soluble, is manufactured by Mono-Sol Corporation and Reynolds Metals Company. Major outlet is in packaging detergents and other materials in which the package and contents are thrown into water for solution.

The United States Food and Drug Administration has approved use of PVA in external cosmetic preparations in concentrations not to exceed 7.5%. It has also been used in low molecular weight grades as a synthetic blood plasma but has proven unsuitable in this application. Polyvinyl alcohol tubing may shortly be used for surgical purposes.

In today's ever increasing concern by state and municipalities over stream pollution PVA offers no problem as it does not pollute.

PHONOGRAPH RECORDS

Vinyl records are large-volume application. Conventional microgroove long-playing records have a sound track which is one mile long. The necessary fidelity requires excellent reproduction from the mold and a material which can be grooved with extreme accuracy and yet retain high scratch resistance.

Vinyl chloride-vinyl acetate copolymer and polystyrene have been competitive for the American phonograph market. The shellac record of some years ago was fragile, heavy, had poor wearing qualities and a very high background noise level. The earlier polystyrenes were poor in abrasion resistance and fair to good in fidelity. Low molecular weight vinyl copolymer is very successful due to its ability to flow rapidly and with high precision into the microscopic cavities necessary for faithful reproduction of the sound track. The vinyl copolymer has replaced polystyrene and no longer considers it a serious challenger. Vinyl compounds based upon formulation requiring little or no plasticizer can produce clear, unbreakable records. Transparent record formulation often uses 97 parts of a low molecular weight vinyl chloride-vinyl acetate copolymer, one-half to one part of a carnauba wax, one-half part of a dye, and 1-2 parts of calcium stearate.

The use of plasticizers and fillers gives lower cost and lower quality records when these ingredients are added in large volume. National Lead recommends a low filler content formulation which is as follows:

Vinyl copolymer	74 parts
Polyethylene glycol ester	4
Filler	16
Carnauba wax	1
Carbon black	2
Tribasic lead sulfate monohydrate	2
Dibasic lead stearate	1

Low-cost record formulations may use as little as 30 parts of vinyl copolymer in conjunction with a number of fillers, plasticizers, paraffins and lubricants. These low cost formulations may use filler contents in excess of 50% and plasticizers of 5% or more.

A number of procedures may be used in preparing the compounds. A popular method is to dry blend in any suitable container, Banbury mix at temperatures not in excess of 300°F, and then worm-extrude to a 2-roll calender. The Banbury and calender cycles generally require no more than 20 minutes. As the stock is removed from the calender it is scored into biscuits. The cold biscuits are separated into individual sections and placed on hot steam tables which preheat the stock to approximately 300°F. The material is molded at 300-350°F., often at a pressure of 1500 psi or more. Under this temperature and pressure the stock is sufficiently mobile to flow in a few seconds into all the grooves and reproduce precisely the minute forms which constitute the sound track. This excellent flow of the vinyls permits high precision and perhaps is the most critical requirement which must be met by this industry. The chrome or nickel-copper record stamper molds the records in 15-30 sec press cycle. After the molding is completed the disks are cooled so that they can be quickly removed from the press without warping or distortion.

The record industry is interested in copolymers which in particular have better heat stability than the 85/15 vinyl chloride/vinyl acetate copolymer available in 1957. A vinyl chloride homopolymer of sufficiently low molecular weight and flow properties comparable to copolymer could be a possible solution to the heat stability problem, but such has not as yet been developed. Any homopolymer must have plasticity comparable to copolymer presently in vogue.

GARDEN HOSE

In the last ten years garden hose extruded of vinyl has grown from an insignificant factor to a dominant position. It is believed that this market in 1957 utilized a minimum of 75% vinyl. Consumption of resin was approximately 25 million lb. The early use of vinyl garden hose was strictly as a rubber substitute, but it is likely that vinyls will completely replace rubber in this market. The weight of today's vinyl hose is approximately half that of double-braided neoprene. The wear resistance of vinyl is definitely superior and has better burst strength than rubber. Vinyl hose has less

(Courtesy Supplex Company)

Figure 5.6. Vinyl watering devices are one of many extrusions of large volume use.

frictional resistance to flow of water and therefore for a given diameter will permit greater rate of flow than rubber. The Borden Company has recently introduced a garden hose flexible in freezing weather and firm on the hottest days. This material is PVC reinforced with nylon cord.

National Lead provides the following formulation for clear garden hose:

Resin	100 parts
Organic ester plasticizer	40
Organic ester epoxide	5
Polyethylene glycol ester	10
"Flomax" 25 (liquid barium-cadmium organic complex)	2.5
Stearic acid	0.5

Opaque garden hose is somewhat similarly plasticized plus the addition of 20-40 parts filler and the replacement of the barium-cadmium stabilizer by dibasic lead phosphite.

Argus Chemical in garden hose and other transparent extrusions recommends the use of their Mark M barium-cadmium complex organic salt for superior heat and light stability. The absence of soapy materials in this stabilizer permits maximum clarity. An Argus formulation is:

Resin	100 parts
Primary plasticizer	30
Isooctyl epoxy stearate	15
Mark M (barium-cadmium complex organic salt)	1.5
Stearic acid	0.5

ADHESIVES

The largest use for polyvinyl acetate emulsions has been the preparation of adhesives. It is uncertain whether adhesive or paint applications will be predominant in 1965. The worth of polyvinyl acetate for flexible adhesives lies in its high strength without the use of organic solvents. The emulsions are colorless, odorless and tasteless when made into adhesives for paper cups and food containers. Many types of adhesives are manufactured including use as binders for textile fibers and paper pulp, can-sealing compounds, rubber cement, ceramic, glass, furniture, leather adhesives and general purpose materials. Laminating applications for cellulose acetate film, "Mylar," polyethylene, metal foil and paper also have extensive sale. Cohesive gauze bandages are prepared by impregnating with a soft, pressure sensitive PVAc. Use as wet-bond adhesives on porous materials including paper, cork, wood and cloth set rapidly.

These emulsions, when used on non-porous materials, are generally best applied by wetting the surfaces with the polymer, allowing the adhesive to dry and then bond by heat and pressure. Although the adhesion to many metals is excellent, it often can be improved by the addition of several percent zinc chloride. Grease-proofness and increase in wet strength results when emulsion is incorporated with paper as a coating or impregnant. A tough or a flexible adhesive bond can be made by variation in formulation. Soft-seals are made which permit easy opening of shipping cases. Heat-sealing and vacuum packaging are other outlets for the adhesives. The currently popular use of flocculants on Christmas trees are applied using polyvinyl acetate adhesives. Mass production of bedroom furniture using PVAc adhesives can completely eliminate I-beams and clamps and result in faster bonding with savings of cost and man-power. Use as a "plastic starch" which withstands many launderings is now established.

Polyvinyl acetate adhesives are the most versatile of any vinyl resins. In addition to emulsions the polymer can be applied in solvent solutions in plasticized or non-plasticized forms. Pigments and fillers may be incorporated if necessary. Most solvent adhesives have high viscosity despite low solids content, and can be brushed, applied with caulking guns or roller-coated if the viscosity permits. Spraying is not usually employed. Despite polyvinyl acetate's moderate resistance to water and solubility in most solvents, resistance to oils and gasoline is outstanding. Solvent retention is particularly tenacious, and maximum bond strength is developed only by the removal of the last traces of the solvent by baking. These materials can develop bond strengths of 30,000 psi, but under continuous stress they fail at substantially lower loads.

PVAc resins resist passage of asphalt and thus are useful in bonding supported vinyl to asphalt-impregnated boards. Solid and emulsion polyvinyl acetate are marketed by Shawinigan as "Gelvas" for use in adhesives, coatings, inks and moldings. These resins are recommended in metallic inks because they are neutral and noncorrosive, have good adhesion to metals, and produce colorless, transparent, high-gloss finishes. They are also suitable for inks containing colored pigments, for printing on cellophane, plastic film and glassine.

National Starch recommends vinyl acetate-acrylic copolymer latex of one micron particle size for adhesives and 0.4 micron for paints. Their "Resyn 2203" has 0.1 micron particles and is recommended for films where gloss is required coupled with good strength and flexibility. Some promising uses are reported to be paper coatings, leather finishes and binders for nonwoven fabrics.

A number of copolymer emulsions which impart a degree of internal plasticization use vinyl acetate copolymerized with higher vinyl esters, acrylates, maleates and fumarates. The largest application of these types is in paints.

Polyvinyl chloride-polyvinyl acetate copolymer emulsion manufactured by National Starch Products does not require additives or thickeners to increase viscosity nor pre-emulsification of plasticizers. This material can be plasticized with monomeric plasticizers or acrylic latices. The material marketed as "Resyn 2507" provides a balanced adhesion between vinyl and polar materials and yet has the good properties of PVC and PVAc in the wet state. It is reported that the material has good wet tack and mechanical stability.

Vinyl-vinylidine adhesives are used in MEK solvent. When dry a strong, transparent film is obtained which is resistant to hydrocarbon and chlorinated solvents, and greases and oils. Applications are where good solvent and water resistance are required.

Vinyl Butyral Adhesives

Vinyl butyral adhesives are prepared in solvent and have high viscosity at low solids content. The well known adhesion to glass is particularly outstanding in these water-white, transparent and light-stable films. In safety glass application vinyl butyral adhesives have their outstanding use, despite their relatively poor water resistance.

Grinding in a pebble mill produces glossy dispersions of resin and pigments. This permits large proportions of pigment to be dispersed in the resin without loss of film strength. Intensive milling decreases the solubility of PVB in organic solvents and also increases the softening temperature. These changes can be minimized during milling by the incorporation of water or alcohol.

Adhesive useful life is approximately 212°F., although exposure at higher temperatures is possible for short periods of time. Plywood lamination in conjunction with phenolics has improved adhesion and the adhesive bond is less brittle. Some application is made as a wood sealer and finisher. Compositions containing 50% butyral resin can be used as a sealer over asphaltic materials to prevent bleeding into top coats. The butyral is often blended with large amounts of low molecular resins, such as rosin or ester gum, and compatible plasticizer for formulation as hot-melt adhesives.

Unlike many vinyl resins, vinyl butyral has good wetting

properties and can be pebble mill ground to develop high gloss. Good foam strength can still be obtained even under conditions of high pigment loading. Organic solvent solubility is increased with intensive grinding, but the resin becomes stiffer as the severity of grinding is increased or prolonged. Changes under milling conditions are minimized when this operation is carried out by wetting with water.

Vinyl butyral-phenolic resin adhesives have their widest application in bonding as a safety glass interlayer. However, the excellent adhesive character of the vinyl butyral-phenolic adhesive (vinyl butyral alone is used with glass) may be used for bonding rubber, cloth, metals to plastics, asbestos boards, paper and cork, as well as glass and ceramics. In conjunction with phenolic resin increasing the ratio of vinyl butyral resin has an adverse effect of decreasing boiling water resistance, while improving tensile and impact strength, and decreasing creep resistance. Vinyl butyral resins applied as a hot melt are used for high-speed bookbinding.

Vinyl Pyridine Latex Adhesive

Vinyl pyridine latex is manufactured by Naugatuck Chemical and General Tire and Rubber Company for use as an adhesive supplement for bonding rayon or nylon fibers and rubber stocks. The Naugatuck product is composed of butadiene, styrene and vinyl pyridine and gives improved adhesion when used with resorcinol-formaldehyde in dip formulas either as the main constituent or in admixtures with other latices. In addition to extensive use in tire cord other applications of the material are in belting, hose, and other mechanical goods.

POLYVINYL BUTYRAL

An estimation of the PVB consumed is difficult due to the limited number of manufacturers and reliable statistics. Consumption in 1957 is believed to be of the order of 18 million lb of resin exclusive of plasticizer. Polyvinyl butyral in automotive safety glass is approximately 2.7 lb of plasticized film per car. Somewhat more diversified use of PVB is being made in fields other than automotive, but this industry still uses perhaps 80% of PVB for safety glass applications (see discussion of PVB under adhesives, this chapter).

Some automobile makers used tempered safety glass in 1958 models to the exclusion of laminated safety glass. Monsanto and duPont have emphasized the safety protection of laminated resin, and are urging that all glass used in cars should be made of it. The sale of the butyral to the auto industry is estimated to be 20 million dollars a year. Union Carbide, although a manufacturer of the polymer, does not manufacture sheeting. Shawinigan Resins Corporation manufacture PVB for Monsanto. All new cars have been required for some years to have laminated safety glass in the windshields but not in side windows. Use of tempered glass is reputed to save the auto manufacturer as much as six dollars per car.

Chrysler Corporation tests vinyl laminated glass by dropping a ½ lb steel ball from a distance of 30 ft onto the surface. Tests are conducted at room temperature and at zero. Glass used in windshields before 1927 was ordinary annealed glass; it was not very resistant to impact, and broke into sharp, jagged, dangerous pieces. The yellowing of the first cellulose nitrate laminate and the poor moisture-resistant quality of its successor cellulose acetate are eliminated by use of PVB. The butyral's adhesion to glass is not diminished by high humidities, offers good light stability and gives clear vision without color development over a long period of time.

It appears likely that the long-term future of PVB in aircraft applications is not good, because at temperatures in excess of 150°F. the PVB glass interlayer bubbles and flows. However, the use of polyvinyl butyral in today's aircraft and automobiles is still not seriously challenged. PVB glass interlayer in airplanes and automobiles can withstand great pressures and sharp blows without rupturing. Safety glass for subatmosphere airplane windows has been subjected to air pressures of 2 tons per sq ft, and although the glass shatters, the air-tight seal of the window is maintained by the PVB interlayer. The tenacious adhesion of the polymer to glass and the toughness of the material are additional safety factors in safety glass. In safety glass, although the glass breaks easily, the PVB interlayer adheres to the glass particles and prevents their dispersal.

Polyvinyl butyral may be prepared by a number of methods. Polyvinyl acetate can be directly condensed with butyraldehyde in the presence of acidic catalysts. Batch operation is believed to be used by all manufacturers for the production of PVB for use in safety glass applications. This may involve batch polymerization of vinyl acetate, its hydrolysis, and finally condensation of polyvinyl alcohol with butyraldehyde.

Plasticizers often employed are triethylene glycol di-2-ethylbutyrate, and di-butyl "Cellosolve" adipate in concentrations of 29-30%. In actual fabrication the dry polyvinyl butyral is mixed with the plasticizer and a suitable solvent, such as alcohol containing stabilizers. Sheets are formed by an extrusion process followed by removal of the solvent. The sheet is provided with an anti-blocking agent and either stored or then laminated after washing to remove the anti-tack agent. duPont is believed to extrude polyvinyl butyral in alcohol solution into water. Heat stabilizers are incorporated in the extrusion compound and are believed to be quaternary amines. Light stabilizers are not used. Glass is carefully cleaned to remove foreign materials and the sandwiched PVB is treated under gentle heat and pressure. Tensile strength of film is reported to be as high as 4,000 psi, and the elongation at break as high as 400%. Polymer for use in safety glass must be free of impurities and carefully stabilized. Some PVB has application as an adhesive and as a primer coat for metal application.

Libbey-Owens-Ford Glass Company in cooperation with Monsanto has developed a method for printing on polyvinyl butyral film. This application utilizes both the silk-screen and rotogravure methods. The resulting product is not only highly decorative but also combines the advantage of safety glass.

Bakelite reports that vinyl butyral resin, when used as a wood sealer under pyroxylin lacquers, makes coatings more resistant to marring and pressure marking due to superior adhesion to the wood. Spread coating to cloth in some cases produces adhesion which exceeds the strength of the fabric. After curing at 300°F., the films are resistant to water, alcohol, acetone and dry-cleaning fluids. Some application has been found as a replacement of rubberized fabric in raincoats and inflatables.

Application in metal-finishing operations in conjunction with phenolic resins improves the flexibility of the base finish. The ratio of vinyl butyral in this application may be one-tenth that of the phenolic, or as much as equal amounts. Bakelite resins applied in clear finishes for exterior exposure can be modified with a urea-formaldehyde resin in a plasticized formulation. Such material gives a clear coating on chromium plate. Incorporation of 10% glyoxal produces air-dry coatings with good solvent resistance.

Resins for lining of cans, drums and tanks provide an even coating and improved adhesion, impact resistance and flexibility of the thermosetting resin incorporated with the butyral. Most can liners are baked at temperatures up to 400°F. for times as long as one hour. The coatings are known as metal conditioners or "wash primers." Thin coatings of the resin are applied in thickness of .0001 to .0005-in. and require only air drying to give a firm bond to the metal surface.

The U. S. Navy has a coating identified as "wash primer WP-1" developed by the Navy in cooperation with Bakelite.

This consists of PVB, basic zinc chromate as a corrosion inhibitor, some extender pigment, phosphoric acid as a catalyst and a solvent for application.

Metal conditioners using PVB can be applied to steel, aluminum, galvanized iron, tin, magnesium and cadmium. The primer can also be applied to concrete. Priming has been used on the steel hulls of ships, railway equipment, automobiles, aluminum house siding, and oil refinery equipment. Wash primers do not replace conventional primers for metal because of the thinness of application, but are generally classed with industrial phosphate metal treatments, and provide temporary protection against rusting and weather exposure. Marine application of steel vessels treated with a wash primer are overcoated with an anti-corrosive vinyl chloride-acetate primer, and then top-coated with a similar polymer. Such a protective coating can withstand sea water for a number of years without repainting. Coating for galvanized iron permits easier covering of outdoor metal paints.

PAINTS

Emulsion-based latex paint sale in 1957 is estimated at 320 million dollars. Approximately 70% of this total latex emulsion production for paint was styrene-butadiene copolymer which was first introduced by Glidden in 1949. Polyvinyl acetate paint emulsions were in excess of 12 million gal. in 1957 and are expected to reach 20 million gal. in 1958. Total latex paint consumption in 1957 was 55-60 million gal. The increase in vinyl acetate based latex paint is more rapid than styrene-butadiene, and it seems apparent that further manufacture of the vinyl will be made at the expense of the older system. Styrene-butadiene paints are not believed to have major exterior application, and the generally excellent acetate paints are expected to acquire a share of this market.

There is no doubt that there is a growing market for vinyl acetate latex paint; this product will realize fantastic gains if most of the predictions made concerning it are accurate. Some observers predict that all automobile paints will be water-based by 1965. A spokesman for Celanese at the Paint Industries Show in October, 1957, stated that water-based paints will increase 70% to 95 million gal. by 1962, and vinyl acetate latex will represent 75% of this volume.

Earliest use of polyvinyl acetate emulsion paint was in Germany and England during World War II, but now the material has a firm foothold on the U. S. paint market. The price differential between styrene-butadiene latex paints and vinyl acetate paints is now negligible. It is logical that the British should have done extensive early work on polyvinyl acetate emulsion paints, as no synthetic rubber production had taken place in England during the war years, and neither styrene nor butadiene monomer was readily available. Nearly all emulsion paints in Britain were plasticized with dibutyl phthalate, and it is believed that this is still extensively used. A shortage of drying oils in Germany led to the discovery that polyvinyl acetate emulsions gave good service as a pigment binder.

Major suppliers of vinyl acetate monomer are Union Carbide, Celanese and Air Reduction, although duPont is believed to produce approximately 50% of the polymer made in the United States. Other major producers of polymer are National Starch, Borden, Shawinigan, Dewey & Almy and Celanese. "Elvacet" polyvinyl acetate emulsion as an exterior and interior paint vehicle is recommended by duPont.

Polyvinyl acetate aqueous dispersions for paints are viscous, white materials containing approximately 55% solids, and of sufficient emulsion stability for formulation into paints. The resin has high pigment-binding capacity and good acceptance for conventional pigments, plasticizers and modifiers. The compounded paints are essentially odorless, colorless, water-insoluble, oil- and grease-resistant and have good film-forming and adhesive properties. Most emulsions in paint application have a pH of 4 to 6, and are composed of microscopically small particles of the resin dispersed in water. These latexes are of a wide range of viscosities from water-thin to extremely viscous. The viscosity range depends on the techniques of polymerization, and the kinds and amounts of protective colloids and emulsifiers used.

Of considerable interest was the announcement in late 1957 that Celanese has developed a high gloss paint based on polyvinyl acetate. Information received from Celanese states that at least five paint companies are making gloss paint based on their technique. Celanese states that their high-gloss polyvinyl acetate latex paint is due to the proper selection of wetting agents and protective colloids, extremely fine particle size, and the proper molecular weight of the polymer in emulsion. The particles are reputed not to touch one another in the dispersion.

Early American work toward the development of vinyl acetate latex paint demonstrated that materials primarily designed for adhesive and textile sizes were poor paint vehicles. The brittleness of homopolymer emulsions was another deterrent, and it was necessary to incorporate plasticizers to obtain the desired degree of flexibility. The wish to eliminate plasticized systems led to more extensive study of copolymers of vinyl acetate. The incorporation of a number of comonomers acts as internal plasticizers and increases film flexibility. Some manufacturers provide a variety of polyvinyl acetate emulsions, but few are suitable for incorporation in paint systems.

A Celanese copolymer emulsion designated CL-202 (possibly a vinyl acetate-acrylate) produces clear, tough, flexible films which have a marked degree of resistance to water spotting. This copolymer in many applications does not require external plasticization. Good storage stability and freeze-thaw stability are reported in paint systems based on this copolymer. The ability to withstand freezing and thawing is of vital consideration to the manufacturers of latex paint. CL-202 has a solids content of 55% and a Brookfield viscosity at 20 rpm and 25°C. of 1,900 to 2,500. The particle size varies from .05 to .40 micron and the pH is 4.0-5.0. Problems in applying paints are minimized at low unreacted monomer content, and it is reported that this material has a maximum monomer content of 0.5%.

Celanese produces a PVAc homopolymer counterpart of CL-202 which is designated CL-102. This material is reported to be intermediate in properties between older type homopolymers and the newer copolymer emulsions. CL-102, when formulated in paints, is reported to give good outdoor weathering performance. Unplasticized 2-mil film has tensile strength between 2,000 and 3,000 psi. Although specific paint formulations are not generally disclosed, it is conceivable that all polyvinyl acetate homopolymer emulsions used in paints are lightly plasticized with possibly 5-10 parts plasticizer.

The Celanese high gloss polyvinyl acetate latex paint formulation for the paint system VG-18 is given in Table 5.1.

Fine particle size is a critical consideration in the formulation of any latex paint, and is one of the keys to superior performance at high pigment volume concentration. Resistance to settling is largely a function of particle size in stable emulsion systems, and the finer this particle size, the less the settling tendency.

Latex emulsions for paint applications contain, in addition to the emulsifiers, various colloids, stabilizers, and other chemicals. Prime and extender pigments are incorporated, as are wetting agents, thickeners, possibly plasticizers, coalescing agents, defoamers, buffers, corrosion inhibitors, mildewcides and fungicides. Prime pigments basic purpose is to provide color and opacity. Pigments widely used are titanium dioxide,

TABLE 5.1. POLYVINYL ACETATE INTERIOR WHITE GLOSS PAINT
USING CELANESE CL-102 AND CL-202

	Pounds	Gallons
20% Daxad 11 Solution	8	.9
Tergitol NPX	3	.3
R & R 551 (water dispersed lecithin)	2	.2
Potassium carbonate	1	—
Titanox RA-50, TiPure R-510, or Unitane OR-540	125	3.6
Amberlac 165 (add incrementally during pigment addition to maintain heavy paste)	100	11.5
	239	16.5

Add in the order listed and mix as a heavy paste for a minimum of 20 minutes, then add:

	Pounds	Gallons
Foamicide 581B	3	.4
Water	*	*
	242	16.9

Disperse on a three-roll mill (Hegman 7 minimum) and letdown in the following order with:

	Pounds	Gallons
Carbitol (add slowly)	40	4.7
	282	21.6

Thoroughly stir into paste for ten minutes

	Pounds	Gallons
Celanese CL-102 } Adjust pH to 8.5-9.0	400	43.5
Celanese CL-202 } with conc. ammonium hydroxide	260	28.4
Water and/or 2% 4000 cps methocel solution (HG grade) (for viscosity adjustment)	59	7.1
	1001	100.6

Weight per gal. — 10.0 lb
PVC — 8.3%
Solids content — 52.0%
Raw material cost — $1.90/gal.
Viscosity — 63-68 KU (overnight)
pH — 8.2-8.7

* *NOTE:* Adjustments for other types of dispersing equipment can be readily made by varying the amount of water in the pigment paste.

lithopone, zinc sulfide and antimony oxide. Reactive pigments such as white lead and zinc oxide are not recommended for today's usage, although it is possible that future latex paints will incorporate them.

Titanium-calcium pigments have been successfully used in amounts less than 2 lb per gal. of paint. This development is not believed to be commercial. Extender pigments tend to flatten a paint; a wide variety of these pigments is applicable, including calcium carbonate, calcium and magnesium silicate, mica, talc, silica and barytes. Mica is being used as an inert pigment for exterior paints and in primer-sealers for film reinforcement. Clays give good flow and high dry hiding in formulations primarily designed for interior application. When clays are used it is desirable that alkaline pigments be used in conjunction with them to maintain a pH of about 8. Talcs contribute to wet abrasion resistance and are sufficiently alkaline for use with clay, as are calcium carbonate and calcium silicate. Calcium carbonate gives good leveling and brush characteristics and has good acceptance in interior paints. Precipitated calcium carbonates are reactive and should be avoided.

Many anionic and nonionic dispersing agents may be used as wetting agents to disperse all pigments and extenders in water before they are added to the emulsion. The wetting agent must have many of the performance requirements made of the polymer and should be stable to normal temperature variations, be effective in the pH range of the paint, and not cause excessive foaming. Combinations of wetting agents are often used, and a popular material is a combination of water dispersed lecithin and sodium salt of polymerized naphthalene sulfonic acid.

Thickening agents help control viscosity and enable the finished paint system to show a minimum of phase separation. One of the most widely used thickeners is methyl cellulose of high purity and high viscosity. High viscosity is desired so that effective thickening can be provided with a minimum amount of additive. Polyvinyl alcohol, alginates, polyacrylate salts, hydroxyethyl cellulose and sodium carboxymethyl cellulose can also be used.

Polyvinyl acetate homopolymer emulsions have varying plasticizer requirements when used in paint systems. The types of wetting agents employed and their amounts are perhaps of primary consideration in determining the required level of plasticizer, although the pigment volume concentration of the paint, the coalescing agents used and the choice of pigments all have a role. Dibutyl phthalate has the greatest acceptance as a plasticizer for polyvinyl acetate homopolymer emulsions, but use is also made of tricresyl phosphate, butyl benzyl phthalate and some of the Paraplexes. Copolymer emulsions are not normally plasticized.

Some vinyl acetate paints use hexylene glycol as a coalescing agent, although Celanese does not recommend its use with either their homopolymer or copolymer emulsion. This additive has a detrimental effect on freeze-thaw stability and also contributes an objectionable odor. Small amounts of coalescing agents improve the adhesion of latex paint to old paint surfaces, permit better film formation at low temperatures and help control the drying rate. Celanese provides interesting data showing the effectiveness of various coalescing agents in order of increasing activity (Table 5.2).

TABLE 5.2. EFFECTIVENESS OF COALESCING AGENTS

Solvent	Activity of Solvent
Water (standard)	1
Ethylene glycol	4
"Carbitol"	5
"Cellosolve"	38
"Carbitol" acetate	92
Butyl "Carbitol"	400
Hexylene glycol	800
Dibutyl phthalate	2,720

A number of the usual defoamers can be used if required in the finished paint, as well as mildly alkaline materials to control pH. It is recommended that the emulsion paint be packaged in suitably coated cans rather than use corrosion inhibitors. Phenyl mercurial salts are effective as a fungicide and mildewcide. A number of water soluble agents can be used, and these materials should be added to the pigment paste.

One of the biggest problems in the preparation of these paints has been to avoid pigment flocculation. This difficulty can be largely avoided by the selection of proper emulsifiers which aid in the dispersion of the pigment. Many commercial aqueous pigment dispersions can be successfully used, and it is generally recommended that nonionic dispersions have preference over anionic materials. When pigment flocculation difficulties arise from use of colored pigments, small amounts of "Tergitol" NP-14 are used to advantage. The lack of compatibility of many oils with alkyds generally eliminate the use of such pigments. Special formulation permits some systems to be used.

Polymer Properties Versus Performance

The best known vinyl acetate paint emulsions of fine particle size and good storage stability must not be subjected to excessive shear during their preparation or coagulation is prominent. National Starch Products has conducted careful studies of the role of high polymers in emulsions and their effect on film properties. These basic findings can be summarized by the effect imparted by large versus small particle size. This work concludes that small particle size of the latex favors film continuity, fusion, scrub resistance, nonsettling, film clarity and high viscosity.

Large particle size favors freeze-thaw and mechanical stability, possibly adhesion and low viscosity. An interrelation of properties versus performance by this same company states that low molecular weight polymer gives high gloss, good fusion and possibly scrub resistance, while high molecular weight polymer has toughness, ease of formulation and freeze-thaw stability. A further report on this factor of freeze-thaw stability relates poor stability to small particle size, low emulsifier concentration, high percent of solids and a soft polymer. Good stability is obtained by large particle size, a high emulsifier concentration, low percent solids and use of a "hard" polymer. Further basic work by National Starch states that gloss decreases steadily as pigment volume concentration increases, while permeability increases as pigment volume concentration increases beyond 42%. Blistering decreases as pigment volume concentration increases beyond 32% and rust formation increases as this figure becomes greater than 42%.

Freeze-thaw Stability. Further mention of freeze-thaw stability should be made. This important characteristic, as well as mechanical and storage stability, is enhanced to a point by the "fineness" of the latex particle size. Some of the earlier homopolymer and copolymer paint emulsions had particle size up to 1.5 microns. Extensive research has been done by Vinly Products Limited, an English operation of Reichhold Chemicals, on the freeze-thaw stability of PVAc emulsion paint. The effect of particle size and molecular weight were investigated. These findings suggest that latex particle size up to 1 micron has slight flocculation which is readily dispersed; particle size of 0.5 micron gives heavy flocculation which is difficult to disperse; 0.5 micron particle size of lower molecular weight than similar particle size material of higher molecular weight is precipitated.

The effect of plasticization was studied by incorporating dibutyl phthalate and subjecting the latex to freezing cycles. Latex without plasticizer was stable after ten cycles, as was 7% plasticizer incorporation. Fourteen percent plasticizer thickened after one cycle and precipitated after three, while the use of 20% dibutyl phthalate caused precipitation after a single cycle. Vinyl acetate latex plasticized with 20% chlorinated diphenyl was stable after ten cycles. Studies of the effects of wetting and dispersing agents indicated that the best results were obtained with a mixture of methyl cellulose and sodium polymetaphosphate.

Contrary to some work in the United States, incorporation of ethylene glycol was found to impart only slight improvement in the freeze-thaw stability. It is fairly common practice to improve this property by incorporating typical "antifreezes" such as ethylene glycol, propylene glycol and diethylene glycol. Perhaps the most notable surface active agent which contributes to this stability is water-dispersible soya lecithin.

Celanese in an advertisement illustrates that 30 billion polyvinyl acetate particles can be held on the head of a straight pin. There is a point of disagreement between polyvinyl acetate latex paint manufacturers which does not clearly demonstrate whether a fine particle size latex or a somewhat larger particle size has greater potential.

Application of Paints

Vinyl acetate latex paints can be applied by any of the conventional methods due to their good flow and brushability. Excellent formulation is necessary so that brush marks will be eliminated. Most paint systems dry within thirty minutes and may be recoated in an hour. Objectionable odor is minimized as the paints dry by evaporation of water and are free of oxidative and solvent odors. Early work, some of it in England, indicated that these emulsions can be applied to a variety of exterior surfaces including previously painted wood, masonry surfaces, and glazed and unglazed asbestos shingles.

The ease of application of the latex paints does not minimize the importance of the proper preparation of the surface to be painted: removal of loose scale and dirt is absolutely essential. Tests have shown that vinyl acetate paint can be applied to moderately chalky weathered house paints with no evidence of film failure due to loss of adhesion. Early exterior vinyl acetate paints had poor color retention of tinted paints, but this has been markedly improved. Good resistance to rain, sunlight, and urban, rural, and industrial atmospheres are displayed. Interior paint can be applied to new plaster within a few days due to good alkali resistance and moisture permeability of the film. Fine particle size also aids in film formation and makes for generally better paint. Primer-sealers using polyvinyl acetate emulsion are also well accepted.

The cause and correction of a number of problems which can occur through use of these emulsion paints are known. Paint coagulation or viscosity increase on storage is due to inherent instability correctable by the proper choice and amount of wetting agent. Changes in pH can contribute to paint instability; this can be overcome through use of buffers and proper extender pigments. A high percentage of free vinyl acetate monomer or comonomer can result in problems which are overcome by rigid removal of the unreacted monomer to a maximum content of 0.5%. A viscosity decrease on storage can be due to bacterial attack of the thickening agent, or pigment flocculation. Corrective measures are use of a preservative and a proper dispersing agent, respectively.

Variation in pigment shades can occur on storage and result due to use of an improper pigment or pigment flocculation. The choice of a proper pigment and the use of a good dispersing agent can eliminate this difficulty. Pinholes in the paint film can be caused by entrapped air or foaming during application. Use of an antifoam agent is generally the proper solution, although excess antifoam agent produces fisheyes in the finished paint. Poor adhesion is generally a result of inadequate surface preparation or due to a paint film unusually water-sensitive. If an abnormally high pH of the dried paint film results, metal staining on exterior exposure can occur.

OTHER USES OF POLYVINYL ACETATE

The sizing of textiles by polyvinyl acetate emulsions is old and well established. These emulsions find application with all types of fibers and fabrics including blends of natural and synthetic materials. A soft hand or a crisp, stiff finish may be imparted depending upon the choice of emulsion used. Tensile strength, abrasion resistance and fastness to washing are also contributed. A textile application of importance is for finishing nylon hosiery where a light coating improves snag-resistance, hand, and appearance. The emulsions have also been applied as binders and stiffening agents for felt and straw hats, to increase the stiffness of nylon netting and other fabrics, prevent slippage of thread and prevent edge ravelling. Rugs apply emulsion in back filling, binding and stiffening compounds.

Molded products are not made of polyvinyl acetate alone, although some application is by mixing the polymer with fillers and other resins which improve the form stability.

POLYVINYL CHLORIDE

Wire Extrusions

Extrusion of electrical compounds uses the greatest volume of PVC resin. The two general methods of vinyl extrusions for wire and cable are from a dry blend and hot fluxing. Powder blend extrusions are rapidly gaining in popularity and may well be greatly predominant by the early 1960's. Different extrusion conditions are required for dry blends and granular extrusions, the former usually requiring a lower temperature at the rear of the extrusion cylinder and higher temperatures at the front. It is accepted practice to provide additional screen packing to maintain higher pressures for dry-blended compounds. The choice of dies required for smooth extrusions varies depending on the particular.compound and the technique of extrusion. Dies with longer bearing lengths are recommended by some fabricators. Powder mixing may be performed in simple ribbon blenders or other types of internal mixers, while granulated compounds require mill and Banbury mixing facilities.

(*Courtesy Escambia Chemical Corporation*)

Figure 5.7. Experimental PVC extrusion.

The basic parts of an extruder assembly for wire and cable is a supply reel supplying the extruder through a cross-head, cooling trough, spark tester, capstan and take-up reel. As a compromise between the improvement of fisheyes and the worsening of porosity, extruders with a shallow-flighted screw are sometimes used. Fisheyes, as well as porosity, are generally improved by increasing the back pressure in the extruder. This is probably due simply as a result of better mixing by moving the melt zone farther back in the extruder. Dry blend extrusion requires the extruder to simulate the pre-treatment given the granular compound by Banbury and mills and also to fuse the dry blend.

If the conditions of dry blend extrusion are not satisfactory, fisheyes occur in the extruded product. It is therefore essential that the extruder provide a shearing effect to give an extruded product of high quality. Pressure head valves have been designed to obtain various back pressures on the screws. Work done by a number of companies indicates that porosity from dry blend extrusions will be lessened using modern vented extruders. The vented extruder has not had wide acceptance by the wire industry. Enthusiasm for this type of extrusion is increasing in some quarters.

Two broad classes of compounds are employed in the electrical field: primary insulation for wire coating, and jacketing or secondary insulation for the mechanical protection of primary insulated wires. Primary insulation applied directly over the conductor to provide protection for the electrical system must have a high insulation resistance and good flexibility and electrical properties after long use and exposure. Various selected clays can be incorporated to improve electrical resistance although the amounts of this filler generally cannot exceed 10-15% by weight. Incorporation of greater quantity of clay impairs physical properties and lowers heat stability. Great resistance to deformation is essential so that during handling and installation the wire will not break through the insulation. National Lead Company recommends Tribase (3 $PbO \cdot PbSO_4 \cdot H_2O$), Tribase-E (basic lead silicate sulfate), Lectro "60" (lead chlorosilicate) and Dythal (PbO content 79.8%), for use in primary insulation.

These materials have excellent heat-stabilizing action and outstanding electrical properties. National Lead suggests "Dythal" as the best available stabilizer for coping with the high extrusion temperatures employed and the rigorous heat history encountered in 90°-105°C. appliance wire insulation. This may be due to an unusually low reactivity of the stabilizer with plasticizers under strong heat conditions. DS-207 (dibasic lead stearate) is often used to supplement the primary stabilizer. The material's basic function is to provide lubrication and improve electrical properties during prolonged water immersion.

Secondary insulating or jacketing stocks require less emphasis on insulation resistance, since mechanical protection is their primary function. As jacketing stocks are usually applied in thicker wall section than primary stocks, they must be more flexible. These materials are subjected to greater light exposure and oxidative attack and must be tough, have high abrasion resistance and flame resistance. "Dyphos" (dibasic lead phosphite) and DS-207 is a good combination for use in non-black types. Coprecipitated lead orthosilicate and silica gel have less heat stability than the above, low tinting strength, prevent spewing and have low reactivity toward plasticizers and colorants. These properties adapt them for special electrical applications such as appliance cords, aircraft wire and Christmas tree wiring.

A standard general purpose insulation formulation for primary or jacket applications is supplied by National Lead:

PVC	100 parts
Organic ester plasticizer	50
Filler	10-20
Tribase or Tribase-E	7
DS-207	0-1

Argus Chemical Corporation recommends the use of electrical grade stabilizers of Mark XI (barium cadmium laurate)

and Mark XX (chelating agent) for manufacture of primary
insulation. Recommended formulation for electrical insulation is:

Resin	100 parts
Diester plasticizer	45
Drapex 4.4 (epoxy)	5
Pigment 33 (clay)	10
Antimony oxide	3
Titanium dioxide	1
Mark XI (electrical grade)	2
Mark XX (electrical grade)	1

Outdoor line wire and service drops use wire constructed of
two PVC-insulated conductors intertwined with a central
strand of steel which acts as a ground and also provides
added strength. Automotive electrical systems have nearly
doubled in size and capacity in the last twelve years, some
cars now using more wire than the average home, according
to Buick Division of General Motors Corporation. The 1958
Buick uses nearly 2 miles of wiring compared with about a
mile in cars built at the end of World War II.

Convair reports their new 880 jet passenger liner expected
to make its debut in 1959 will have over 15 miles of vinyl-
insulated wire in its system. Aircraft and automotive applications are used in low tension outlets, tubing, conduits, power
control and communication cable. Applications of vinyls are
in the construction industry in building wire (T and TW),
bell wire and non-metallic sheathed cables. Industrial wiring
is mostly wiring of electrical equipment, machine tools and
low voltage power systems. Utilities use primary insulation
and jacketing, general control cables and other types of
insulation.

The communications industry requires vinyl jackets on
high- and low-frequency cable, telephone and switch-board
wire. Marine applications have used under water wiring,

signal and control systems, and wiring on shipboard. Maximum accepted temperature uses for vinyl insulation in 1957 are in 105°C. applications. Plans are being made to permit use of PVC in 125°C. wire applications. The use of vinyls in the electrical industry is growing at a rapid rate, however, this rate will be even more accelerated if 125°C. outlets are permitted.

The excellent insulation resistance of PVC has in some cases permitted the thickness of the insulation to be reduced, which makes for even greater economic value. Some of the earliest insulated wire has shown little wear or deterioration since its installation. Long exposure in water has also given good aging characteristics. The excellent chemical resistance of PVC to many chemicals and corrosive materials has enabled insulated wire and cables and jacketed cables to give excellent service in highly corrosive soils and in chemical plants. In addition to good water resistance of PVC, the oxygen and ozone resistance is sufficiently good to provide the required service life. Certainly one of the primary characteristics of value is the flame resistance, which can be complemented even further by the choice of plasticizer and compounding ingredients.

Plasticizers generally have poorer electrical resistance than the resin itself. A plasticizer should be strongly hydrophobic and nonpolar, and stable toward hydrolysis. Judicious choice of plasticizer can give good service properties over a wide range of temperature, resistance to migration, good physical properties, good flame and chemical resistance, while reducing the insulation resistance as little as possible.

Fillers do improve electrical resistance up to about 15% loading, above which the electrical properties suffer. When larger amounts of clays are added, their sole function is to cheapen the product. As the amount of fillers is increased, the tensile strength, elongation, and abrasion resistance are decreased. Coupled with these is an increase in specific gravity, moisture absorption and brittleness. Calcium carbonate in some electrical applications competes with clay fillers.

The choice of pigments must also be judicious to avoid severe deterioration of electrical properties. Dibasic lead stearate is one of the preferred lubricants as it permits increased extrusion rates and also provides a degree of stabilization for the formulation.

Plasticizers in the wire and cable industry are believed to be approximately 65% phthalates, 15% phosphates, 10% polymeric, and the remainder low-temperature types and miscellaneous materials.

Electrical insulating films and tapes are a relatively new application and Minnesota Mining, and others visualize growing vinyl use in such materials.

Injection Molding

Injection molding of PVC dry blends is becoming increasingly popular. The advent of plastic materials which would more readily lend themselves to injection molding, coupled with improved design, should permit this industry to realize growth. The electrical industry in various applications has been a good customer for molded vinyl articles. One of the best known applications is in the manufacture of a number of parts for vacuum cleaners. Perhaps the largest molded outlet is in portable electrical cord plugs. This field could easily utilize 15 million lb or more of PVC by 1960. Other applications are in various yoke insulators, nipples, electrode handles, gaskets, bumper strips for various appliances and corrosion-resistant coverings.

Injection molding of flexible vinyls has been successfully adapted by the automotive industry. Granulated PVC prepared by Banbury mixing is followed by a milling operation. Injection molding temperatures are variable over a range of 300 to perhaps 400°F., at pressures up to 25,000 psi or more, and for short time cycles. The amount of plasticizer generally chosen for flexibles is about 50 parts, with liberal use of various stabilizers such as the barium-cadmiums in concentrations of 4 parts or higher. Typical lubricants such as calcium stearate are used in 0.5 to 1 part levels. The plastisols, when injection-molded, are generally molded at temperatures approximately that of suspension resin, but usually at somewhat lower pressures. The plastisols do require longer molding time cycles to develop optimum physical properties.

Injection molding of rigid vinyl is a much more difficult operation and requires a high degree of plastic flow, extensive use of stabilizers, high heat stability under the conditions used and special mold design apparatus.

Injection-molded pipe fittings of unplasticized polyvinyl chloride was announced in 1957 by Tube Turns Plastics. The new fittings reportedly will match the burst strength of Schedule 40 PVC pipe and will cost about one-third less than the regular line of standard heavy wall (Schedule 80) industrial fittings. The fittings will be made of both Type I and Type II materials. Although little has been done to date rigid injection molding of butadiene-styrene-acrylonitrile and PVC (Type II) has promise.

Vinyl Monofilaments

The extrusion of vinyls in the form of monofilaments (other than saran and in acrylonitrile copolymers) is of relatively minor importance. However, the vinyls can be extruded in a manner somewhat similar to that used for saran. The important feature in this extrusion is one of design of the extruder head and die components, so that entrapment and resulting decomposition of the vinyl will not occur. The use of breaker plates and screens must be avoided to minimize back pressure, which would result in excessive frictional heat. Bakelite has provided data for producing a 0.014 in. diameter monofilament as follows:

Extrusion Temperatures

Worm	120-160°C.
Feed end	cold
Back cylinder	135
Front cylinder	155
Head	155
Die	155
Screen sizes	none

After the completion of each extruder run it is necessary to clean the extruder thoroughly so that no polymer residue remains. Stretching and orienting is in a room temperature water bath which will permit about a 60 in. travel of the filament in the cooling bath. The vinyl monofilaments may be oriented continuously or wound on spools to be oriented later. Stretching of 575-650% in boiling water is recommended, while annealing may be performed under constant tension in boiling water. The annealed vinyl monofilament is reported to have the following physical properties:

Tensile strength, psi	30,000-40,000
Knot strength, psi	14,000-24,000
Elongation, %	20-30
Shrinkage in 20 min at 65°C., %	4-5

POLYVINYL FORMAL

This condensation product of polyvinyl alcohol and formaldehyde has its most extensive application in the manufacture of tough, heat-resistant wire enamel. "Formvar," made by Shawinigan, is combined with an alkyl phenolic resin in a solvent mixture of cresylic acid or furfural and naphtha. After application of the material to wire, the coating is cured to a cross-linked state. Solenoid coils are bonded by a solution of polyvinyl formal applied in ketone or ester solution. The "Redux" adhesive process has been used in airplane construction in which surfaces are first coated with phenolic resins, dusted with polyvinyl formal, and cured under heat and pressure to give greater structural strength than welding or riveting. The formal and phenolic resins in solution are applied as cements in bonding metal to metal. Other applications are in metal coatings for food can linings and a steel priming composition. The polymer has had minor use in the manufacture of phonograph records. The plasticized composition forms tough, elastomeric compositions for such uses as self-sealing gasoline tanks for aircraft and non-marring hammer heads. Calendering and extrusion of sheet stock has been accomplished.

Products injection molded from polyvinyl formal are tough, rigid and dimensionally stable. The types of "Formvar" for molding are presented in Table 2.9 (p. 48). It is essential that all molding powders be thoroughly dried prior to use. Pan drying for two hours at 180°F. is satisfactory. Compounds for molding applications usually require calcium stearate lubricant and *p*-tertiary amylphenol as a stabilizer. A plasticizer is occasionally used.

The ingredients should be dry blended and compounded in a Banbury mixer or a two roll plastic mill at a stock temperature of 300-350°F. In most instances injection pressures in excess of 20,000 lb are required, while stock temperatures vary from 350 to 450°F. At molding temperature the polymer has a high viscosity and "pin-point" gating is not recommended. These materials have varied notched Izod impact strengths of 0.6 to 20 ft-lb/in.

Compounding for extrusion is done by mixing polyvinyl formal and a solvent, allowing the material to soak for several hours and then slowly agitating. A desirable solution is a mixture of polar and nonpolar solvents. Extrusions can be conducted in conventional equipment at temperatures of 320 to 380°F.

No experimental explanation of the curing mechanism of polyvinyl formal and phenolics has been advanced prior to a paper by Shawinigan in *Industrial and Engineering Chemistry* (February, 1958). These findings indicate that phosphoric acid catalyst effects cross-linking of polyvinyl formal molecules at 175°C. in 30 min. This appears to result by self-condensation through the hydroxyl groups associated with the formal. The hydroxyl groups also cross-link by co-condensation with phenolic methylol groups. Some hydrolysis of acetate resin also associated with "Formvar" results from self- and co-condensation between polyvinyl formal and phenolic methylol groups.

VINYL TILE AND FLOORING

Vinyl flooring using vinyl chloride-vinyl acetate copolymers and vinyl chloride homopolymer is rapidly approaching resin use of a hundred million pounds annually. This industry a few years ago was in the parallel position that vinyl foam and rigid vinyl find themselves today. Glowing predictions were made of the vast volume consumption of vinyl resin to be used in flooring, but much more time was required to develop and sell this flooring than the optimistic sources predicted. Now, it seems quite likely that vinyl flooring will continue to make vast strides, and volume use well in excess of 100 million pounds by 1965 is predicted.

Estimates are variable of the consumption of resin in flooring for 1957. It is likely that the total in this category was approximately 85 million lb, although one flooring manufacturer indicated usage in 1957 was 70 million lb. This industry has moved at an extremely rapid pace as mass production of vinyl type flooring began after World War II. U. S. Tariff Commission figures for 1953-1957 indicate 25, 34, 56, 66, and 81.4 million lb per year, respectively, were consumed. This industry has more than doubled in the three year period since 1954.

Vinyl resins are in direct competition with various hard

surface flooring materials in domestic and commercial use. A practically unlimited color possibly can be made. These floorings show even wear when subjected to heavy use and are readily cleaned by conventional methods.

The resins are used to produce five different types of floor coverings:

(1) Vinyl asbestos tile
(2) Press-polished homogeneous tile
(3) Printed or enameled rug types
(4) Felt-based
(5) Linoleum

Vinyl asbestos tile is believed to represent perhaps 60% of the total vinyl usage in floor coverings. Press-polished tile may represent 20-25% of the remainder.

The flooring industry refers to binder components as including resin, plasticizer and stabilizers. The amount of resin used varies widely depending upon the type of tile desired. Vinyl chloride/vinyl acetate copolymer (85/15) sometimes used is approximately 25% of the total formulation. A typical vinyl asbestos floor tile formulation recommended by Argus Chemical is as follows:

Vinyl copolymer (85/15)	50
Asbestos	50
Atomite	80
DOP	9
Titanox	6
"Paraplex" G-62	1.25
Mark 225 (a magnesium stabilizer)	3

The addition of a color pigment is optional.

Harshaw recommends their barium-cadmium and barium-zinc stabilizers for resilient systems and barium for asbestos.

Vinyl asbestos tile is processed in the same equipment utilized by asphalt tile manufacturers. The mix is Banbury-mixed and then milled at temperatures of 200°F. or higher.

Slabs are cut from the mill and passed through a series of calenders operating at approximately 200°F. the last calender in the series being gauged to finish the stock in the desired thickness. After cooling the material is cut to shape.

National Lead suggests a formulation for semi-rigid asbestos stock:

Resin	100
Organic ester plasticizer	60
Organic ester epoxide	10
Asbestos filler	140
Filler (other than asbestos)	130
"Titanox" RA-50	25
Lead salicylate	7
Barium-cadmium stabilizer	2
Calcium stearate	1

National Lead's heavy duty asbestos semi-rigid formulation:

Vinyl copolymer (low molecular wt.)	100
Organic ester plasticizer	20
Plasticizer (low temperature type)	5
Chlorinated paraffin	10
Asbestos filler	100
Filler	250
"Titanox"	10
Lead salicylate	6
Tribasic lead sulfate	2
Lead stearate	1

Most asbestos fillers are fibers of short length and although longer fibers are better, they are more expensive. To prevent the asbestos fiber from being broken during mixing, this material is usually added as late as possible in the mixing operation. As would be expected, DOP has good acceptance as a plasticizer. The choice of plasticizer and stabilizer is an important consideration. Impurities such as iron associated with the asbestos and other materials can cause staining of the finished product, and therefore the stabilizer system used must compensate for these impurities. Ferro Chemical recommends their barium-zinc stabilizers ("Ferro 1972" or "Ferro Permyl" A) when clay, asbestos, or other filler containing contaminant iron is used.

Vinyl tiles may be prepared as a single layer of a highly filled compound and also by lamination of an unfilled top layer over a low-cost and highly filled backing. Homogeneous tile (no asbestos) is of exceptionally high quality. The binder content of these tiles varies from 35 to 45% while the filler content is approximately 55-65%. Homogeneous tile is prepared by an internal mixing operation utilizing a plasticized (approximately 10%) vinyl resin, clay and whiting filler, and stabilizers. The stock is then milled and marbleized on the last mill, removed and pressed, or delivered to a calender followed by a pressing and cooling operation. Some tile manufacturers are believed to press continuously from a calender utilizing a series of polished drums. The sheeted material is sanded or milled on the reverse side to the desired thickness. Some tile is manufactured of a laminate applying a vinyl formulation overlayer to a highly loaded and relatively cheap backing.

The linoleum industry has used some vinyl polymers in their formulation. The polymer replaces rosin totally or in part and is mixed with linseed oil which is oxidized. Wood flour or ground cork and pigments complete the composition, and the material calendered onto cotton or asphalted felt, followed by lengthy curing. Some German linoleum development has utilized a binder for linoleum of 10% vinyl latex.

Felt based vinyl flooring applies a laminate of film or sheeting to an asphalt impregnated felt base. When unsupported films are used, a latex sealer is necessary to prevent discoloration due to the asphalt. This development is believed to have been first accomplished by Armstrong Cork Company. Vinylfelts are cheap to produce and possibly may realize greater growth. Another inexpensive product is made by printing utilizing an ink onto a covered asphalt-felt and the whole coated with an organosol.

The fear of medical personnel that static electricity will cause explosions has been minimized by the installation of conductive vinyl tile in hospital operating rooms. Some floor tile supplied by Robbins Floor Products requires no adhesive as the tiles are secured by lateral compression, and the rigidity of the tile to its support is developed by waffle-like pockets cut in the underside of the tile.

Fire-resistant wall tile is composed of resin, plasticizers, asbestos, other fillers and color pigments. This material is usually $\frac{1}{16}$ inch thick. The wall tile is cemented in a manner somewhat akin to floor tile. The wall tile should not be installed over new plaster until the surface is completely dry. Armstrong has developed a vinyl-cork tile which applies a clear plastic wearing surface by fusion under heat and pressure to a base of textured cork. Good durability is provided, and the material is resistant to moisture, soap, oil, grease, and alkalies. This same company has a wall and countertop that is of an all-vinyl composition with a "hydrocord" backing. It is particularly recommended for kitchens, and is reputed not to buckle under heat nor crack from bending and stretching. The resilient surface provides a quiet medium when used as countertops.

Fillers

Fillers are important to the vinyl industry. Asbestos has an important role in floor tile, while clays are incorporated in low to high amounts. Fillers are also used to lower compound costs, and for such calcium carbonate is of importance. Some materials combine a dual function of acting also as stabilizers. This class is primarily lead salts. Lead carbonate and sulfate when used in this dual role frequently are loaded as high as 10%. Flame resistance can be improved by the addition of antimony trioxide as well as chlorinated paraffins. Clays are widely used to improve the insulation properties of electrical compounds.

AUTOMOTIVE AND AIRCRAFT APPLICATIONS

A survey by the United States Department of Agriculture states that vinyl consumption in passenger cars has increased from 5 to 45 million lb in the last 5 years. This survey predicts the use to taper off except in the lowest priced models, while backed and non-backed nylon is expected to show growth. It is not clear whether this report refers to all "vinyls" or is restricted to certain resins for specific applications.

In this volume reference has been made to the extensive use of vinyl coated wire in automobiles and aircraft, polyvinyl butyral in safety glass, injection-molded flexible parts and a prediction by a few observers that all auto paints will be vinyl acetate-based by 1965. Vinyl foams are used in cushioning and crash pad applications, while vinyl-metal laminates have outlets. Saran seat covers continue to be used in volume. Vinyl-coated fabric, clear sheeting and many extruded items are used in large volume. Rigid vinyls for duct work are being constructed of rigid plastisols. Strippable coatings for protecting chrome and steel during transit are becoming increasingly popular. Injection molding of lamp gaskets provides a cost saving over rubber parts where flash and trimming operations are required. The grease and solvent resistance make plastisol gaskets for air cleaners on carburetors attractive. Vibrational noises are minimized by the dipping of certain metal parts in solution resins.

Chrysler was the first to experiment with flexible vinyl sheet for convertible rear windows. This is a production item on some 1958 cars. Better rear vision and more light is obtained than with conventional glass windows. The material can be folded into the recess without cracking when the top is down. The material remains flexible in freezing weather, and can be de-iced by merely punching the sheet from the inside.

Automotive wire is required to withstand 600 volts without breakdown. Vinyl-coated wire in Chrysler tests has withstood 10,000 volts or more. Resistance to changes in aging, weathering and corrosive atmospheres, its inertness to gasoline, oils, chemicals and water, its hot and cold stability and wear resistance make its application in automobiles desirable. Chrysler consumes approximately 2 million feet of vinyl-coated wire per day.

Vinyl coatings for steering wheels permit longer wear before the paint is worn off. Coatings permit floor mats for autos to last the life of the car. Rubber floor mats formally uncoated gave poor abrasion resistance.

Boeing is making extensive use of vinyls in their new aircraft. Film and sheeting has been used in virtually the entire interior and vinyl-aluminum laminates have met with favor because of their light weight and good wear qualities. Extensive application is being made by Boeing in their new 707 passenger jet. Coated wire is used in volume.

SLUSH AND ROTATIONAL MOLDING

The total volume of resin consumed by this industry in 1957 was approximately 20 million lb. Plastisols generally are becoming of increased importance, and slush and rotational molding operations are a growing segment of dispersion resin application. Plastisol formulations of today are applicable to either molding application. Superior flow characteristics have been developed which permit more uniform reproduction. The term "plastigel" simply means a plastisol to which any of a number of gelling agents have been added. A popular material is aluminum stearate. Depending upon the formulation the plastigel will vary in viscosity from fluidity to a putty-like consistency. Plastigels are used primarily in the manufacture of toys, while slush molding finds outlet in the fabrication of boots, toys and dolls' heads, etc.

Slush molding produces hollow, flexible articles by use of a mold which is filled with plastisol, heated to fusion, and the excess fluid non-adjacent to the mold wall drained off. Further fusion or curing may be provided until the article is removed from the mold. Many layers may be built up in the mold by repeated filling and curing. It is important in slush molding that the plastisol be of medium viscosity to permit ready filling and draining of the mold. These moldings often require higher heat stability than is characteristic of dip coatings, as higher curing temperatures are often involved.

Slush molded plastisols incorporated with a variety of plasticizers are fabricated into rainboots of good pliability and softness which can be used in summer rain or in snow. Plastisols have been used since about 1951 to fabricate low pressure inflated bumper guards for use as shock cushions for automobiles. This semi-novelty application has resulted in limited sale which does not appear to be growing.

Rotational molding is designed to permit the mold to be rotated in three dimensions, which distributes the plastisol throughout the contour of the mold. Careful selection of plasticizers is required to permit the finished product to be of good quality. High-speed rotational molding is an important factor in the toy and doll industries. Casting machines are of all orders of complexity and number of cavities, some machines permitting a 75-in. molding area or more. The plastisol composition is charged to each cavity mold in the casting machine, and the material rotated in the molds while being fused in a heated oven. If the finished material is to be inflated, this is done, and the article sealed.

Vinyl rotational molding in large volume is only about five years old. Akron Presform Mold Company states that with rotational molding greater control over cross sections, surface quality, detail and weight are provided than by slush casting processes. Further savings are effected in lower labor costs, reduced floor space required, increased output, automatic operation and a reduced number of rejects. Many toys, certain footwear, novelty articles, shoe heels, dolls, basketballs and protective helmets have been made utilizing rotational molding techniques. Plastisol skins applied to ice cream freezer lids in stores substantially reduce replacement of the lids. Rotational castings of battery service kits for filling stations are formed in one piece by Sun Rubber Company.

Rigid plastisols have been made of Shore Durometer of 75 (D scale). Rotational molding of rigid plastisols has formed a one piece defroster distributor duct for automobiles.

Dispersion grade PVC is compression-molded in a patented development by Clark, Cutler and McDermott Company which is finding wide spread use to prevent industrial machinery from transmitting vibration. A damping pad for placing under heavy machinery subject to vibration lowers maintenance costs and improves employee efficiency. The material called "Air-Loc" incorporates dispersion grade PVC with sisal and granulated cork fused into an integrated pad. The pads placed under machines as supports greatly reduce noise and vibration and permit installation of the equipment without bolting or cementing. Use has been made to support such equipment as textile looms, punch-presses, electric motor mounts, printing presses, pumps, many machine tools, extruders, mills, etc. The mixture of resilient cork and long sisal fibers is thoroughly saturated with a dispersion of PVC and plasticizers. The material is compression-molded under great heat and high pressure to produce a pad having a grid-like and embossed surface. A high coefficient of friction (0.7) means that a 20,000-lb load requires a 1,400 lb sidewise force to move it. "Air-Loc" can take a 13,000 psi load without deformation. The material is tough and yet remains flexible as the pad recovers 99% of its original thickness even after repeated loadings to 1,000 psi. It is reputed that about 85% of measurable vibrations are eliminated. Applications have been made varying from light loads to heavy machinery weighing 150 tons.

A new application of "Air-Loc" is being investigated by the railroads to minimize friction between ties and tie plates. Over 200,000 friction-reducing tie pads have been installed for this purpose. Another railroad application uses the pads as a mounting for diesel motors and cradles on tank cars. Use of the pads under machinery permits the equipment to be simply moved to another location if desired.

SOLUTION COATINGS

The entire protective coating industry in 1957 consumed approximately 35 million lb of PVC and copolymer resins. Plastisols and organosols are not strictly considered to be solution coatings, and this discussion will be restricted to coatings of vinyl chloride-vinyl acetate copolymers. These copolymers can be dissolved in organic solvents such as esters, ketones and chlorinated hydrocarbons, and form a protective film by solvent evaporation. The coatings are characterized by absence of odor, taste and toxicity, and are not attacked at normal temperatures by alcohol, oils, aliphatic hydrocarbons, mineral acids and alkalies. Coatings are tough and flexible and have low water vapor permeability and low water absorption. Bakelite VYHH is perhaps most widely used for this application. The constitution of VYHH is approximately 87% vinyl chloride and 13% vinyl acetate. A 15-20% solution of resin can be made in a 1:1 solvent ratio of ketone and aromatic hydrocarbon. Pigments are generally used in the form of a vinyl resin pigment paste. Plasticizers, and heat and light stabilizers are often incorporated in the formulation.

(*Courtesy Bakelite Company*)

Figure 5.8. Parade float produced with sprayed solution of vinyl chloride-acetate resin.

Coatings develop adhesion to smooth surfaces after baking at 325-350°F., while on rough surfaces a mechanical bond is established. Can linings, paper coatings, marine antifouling paints, masonry coatings, and coatings for foil and cardboard are major uses. When the limited heat stability and chemical resistance of a 13-15% vinyl acetate copolymer coating is inadequate, resins of lower vinyl acetate content are often used. However, the lower vinyl acetate resin content reduces the solubility of such copolymers.

Formulation of solution copolymer seldom requires more than 25% phthalate plasticizer based on the resin weight. Pigments are used in varying amounts, depending upon the choice of pigment and the formulation desired. Certain pigments are sometimes used in greater weights than the resin. Pigment dispersions are most often prepared by dry mixing of the resin, pigment, plasticizer and possibly a dispersing aid. Thorough mixing is by grinding on differential speed two-roll mills at as low a temperature as practicable. The stock is broken and cut with a thinner to form pigment paste, generally by rolling the mixing container on a can-roll.

Cast film prepared from copolymer resin in solution and also from plastisol homopolymer is described elsewhere in this chapter.

DISPERSION RESINS

The types and properties of dispersion resins are discussed in Chapter 2. This class of vinyls is made by emulsion polymerization of vinyl chloride. The majority application is in plastisols which incorporate stabilizers, fillers, wetting agents, gelling agents, resin and plasticizer. Major use is in rotational and slush moldings, spraying, knife, and reverse roll coatings, hot and cold dips, extrusions, and chemically and mechanically blown foam. Sprayable plastisols usually are highly thixotropic in the low shear range and possess non-dilatant flow at high shear.

Plasticizers for vinyl dispersions are of both solvating and nonsolvating types. The choice of plasticizer or plasticizers depends upon the type of fabrication and properties desired of the manufactured article. Solvating types swell the resin and permit rapid fusion, which is generally characterized by

poor viscosity stability of the plastisol. Nonsolvating plasticizers do not cause this swelling tendency and permit slower
fusion and good shelf stability.

A great number of phthalate ester plasticizers are used in
dispersion resins. A wide range of properties can be obtained
depending upon the choice of plasticizer. Adipate plasticizers
produce characteristics of the finished article somewhat parallel to their use with suspension vinyls. These materials give
good low-temperature characteristics. Phosphates are used
primarily for their flame-resistant character. Epoxy plasticizers can be incorporated to provide viscosity stability, good
migration resistance, and superior heat stability. Secondary
plasticizers of limited compatibility generally produce low
viscosity and must be used with caution to avoid massive
plasticizer migration.

Plastisol Compounding

Plastisols may be compounded in any shear type mixer.
The choice of the mixer is dictated by the consistency of the
material. Those of moderate consistency can be conveniently
handled in a Hobart or Ross apparatus. Heavier-duty mixers
are Abbe and Baker-Perkins. It is desirable that the viscosity
of the material be kept at a minimum. This requires cooling
or an intermittent mixing cycle as excessive heat buildup has
an adverse effect on the viscosity. In one type of operation
a portion of the plasticizer is added to the mixer with agitation, and the dispersion resin is slowly mixed in. Fillers pre-
dispersed in plasticizer are then added, and finally the remaining plasticizer containing stabilizers.

Plastisols increase in viscosity upon storing, but most formulations reach relatively stable viscosity levels after several
days. Surface-active agents in conjunction with plastisols
provide lower paste viscosity. Some of the more effective
materials are diethyleneglycol mono-butyl ether, polyalkylene
glycol esters, dioctyl sodium sulfosuccinate and lecithin.

Deaeration of the plastisol is particularly necessary for slush-molding applications, this deaeration being best effected by application of a vacuum on a thin layer of the plastisol. Materials of heavy consistency do not lend themselves to this method of deaeration but are masticated on a three-roll mill which mechanically removes entrapped air. A fusion temperature of 350°F. is perhaps the most widely accepted temperature, while the times of fusion vary from the briefest of contact to nearly an hour. Many types of heating including dielectric are used by different fabricators.

Plastisols can be applied by a variety of methods. A typical formulation used in coatings is 100 parts of the dispersion resin with 60-80 parts of a mixture of monomeric and polymeric plasticizers. The polymeric plasticizers are generally in a considerably lower volume than monomeric. Other ingredients, such as clays, titanium dioxide and stabilizers, are used in amounts of 45-50 parts. Plastisol coatings for spread applications to paper and textiles apply either a knife-coating technique or reverse roll coating. Knife coating may take the form in which the material to be coated is supported by a drum or stationary bed as it passes under the knife and is continuously coated by use of an endless rubber blanket revolving on two rolls, one on either side of the knife. A floating knife coating method is most widely used and is perhaps the simplest. The textile or other material passes over a support and then under the unsupported knife, which is under tension, and finally over an idler roll. Reverse roll coating applies the dispersion resin on the backing medium by a roll rotating in the direction opposite to that of the web. Widespread use of this technique is made in paper coating and assures good control of gauge.

Dip coating permits heavy deposition of the plastisol on many materials and shapes. The protective coating of the resin is applied by either a cold or a hot dip, and it is reported that cold dips permit deposition of a single coat as thick as

100 mils. Hot dipping gives somewhat better control of the thickness by varying the temperature. Multiple dippings may be made in both cold and hot applications.

Materials can be dip-coated as thin as 1 mil with good control of thickness. This method is used to a large extent in the preparation of gloves. A suggested dip formulation provided by Monsanto is:

"Opalon" 410	100	parts
DIDP	50	
"Santicizer" 160	25	
HB-20	20	
"Aroclor" 1254	20	
Harshaw 128-V-5	2	
Harshaw 8-V-1	0.5	
"Santocel" 54	3	

Metals such as wire, coils and baskets, various bolts and soft gloves are major outlets for this application.

Protective vinyl coatings for metal have been used since 1943, but have only recently obtained major sale. This market is estimated for 1957 to be approximately 10 million dollars. This, of course, is a very small proportion of the industrial finish market, but the prospect is encouraging.

Organosol applications form a harder coating than plastisol, but are limited in that the thickness of application is substantially less than by plastisol. Organosols are rarely applied in greater thickness than 10 mils. Application of the dispersion to metal can be by dipping or spraying of a plastisol using conventional spray guns. After this application, curing of the coating is accomplished at 350°F. to produce a tough, continuous film with thicknesses up to ¼ in. in a single spray application. Dipping a metal into a plastisol bath is an excellent means of application. The metal fixtures are preheated to baking temperatures and dipped into the plastisol, followed by oven baking. This "hot dip" technique has a counterpart in a "cold dip" which is similar, except the plastisol is applied at room temperature followed by curing. Vinyl-coated metals have good anti-corrosion properties; the highly abrasion-resistant finishes have sound insulating characteristics, are resistant to oils and moisture, and provide a degree of chemical resistance. Coatings are applied to such diverse articles as tanks and baths, gloves, clothes lines, dishwashing machines, office furniture, fiber glass, screening, tapes, refrigerator shelving, automobile dashboards and kick panels, cables, wiring harnesses and many novelty applications.

Plastisols applied by any means effectively prevent deterioration of the metals which they coat. Items which are too large to be dip-coated are often sprayed. Spray applications for large metal air scrubbers for use in coal mines as well as flag poles have been coated. Perhaps the major limitation imposed today upon spray coating of plastisol resins is finding ovens of suitable size to permit curing.

Sprayable plastisol compounds are offered which can be applied to metal surfaces without need of primer undercoats. Vinyl-coated "Fortisan" has been introduced by Herculite Protective Fabrics and may be an application of a vinyl plastisol. Metal and Thermit has developed a sprayable plastisol which produces film thicknesses up to 50 and 60 mils per spray coat. Pore-free coatings can be applied without seams or joints where corrosive materials might penetrate. The electrical insulating properties and acoustical properties are good. Perhaps the primary advantage of spray plastisols is the convenience of application over dip coatings when the object to be coated is very massive. Strippable vinyl plastisols are used to offer temporary protection against atomic radiation. The plastisol can be spray-applied, and after contamination of walls and equipment readily stripped off the surface and destroyed.

(*Courtesy Brookhaven National Laboratory*)

Figure 5.9. Vinyl "cocoon" sprayed on a "hot cell" is stripped and discarded after contamination.

Polished metal parts of chromium and stainless steel for automobile trim can be conveniently protected by strippable plastisols. This procedure has partially eliminated the costly and time-consuming operation of packing the parts singly in paper tubing.

Plastisol coatings can be made into thick sheets such as

those used for conveyor belts to thin transparent film for table cloths, tapes and chintz. The base in these operations varies according to the desired use and can be nylon, cotton fabrics, paper, jute, glass, asbestos, etc. Plastisol paste operation for fabric coatings are often of high viscosity while low viscosity

(*Courtesy Michigan Chrome & Chemical Company*)

Figure 5.10. A plastisol coated agitator for a waste disposal system.

pastes are desired for dip operations. Vinyl-coated fabrics utilizing plastisol, organosol, latex and application of suspension resin as film and sheeting is described in Chapter 4.

Michigan Chrome and Chemical now uses a dip coating tank which contains over 6,000 gal. of plastisol. This large dip application has been used for coating mixers, for slurry tanks and anodizing racks. Racks and baskets dip coated with plastisol can be effectively used without deterioration at high acid concentrations encountered in plating operations due to their chemical resistance.

Decorative awnings are produced from organosols by first applying a colorless base coat of the organosol to the fabric; then a second top coat which is colored is added from a second organosol; the top coat is then fused by heat to the base coat. A new application is the manufacture of artificial flowers and foliage. The plastisol is added to intricate metallic molds and cured using either single or multi-colors. This application produces artificial plants which are most life-like in appearance. A plastisol application of major potential is in plastic-lined crowns for bottles and closures. A substantial quantity of cork has already been replaced.

PVC plastisol is used as gaskets for oil and air filters. This type of gasket is being adopted by automobile manufacturers due to the excellent life of the gasket material and the ease of assembling compared to conventional rubber gaskets. An application of potential is the use of cast plastisol for joints for vitrified clay sewage pipe. In the installation of 24-in. clay pipe approximately 11 lb of plastisol are used for the two gaskets on each section. Rigid plastisols are a new development and offer potential of large volume use. A novel application is made by Histoslide Company who fabricate anatomical models for medical demonstration. Realistic representation of the human body is provided by incorporation of semi-rigid and flexible plastisols and foamed vinyls.

U. S. Rubber Company has reported that a novel all-weather storage building which is supported by low-pressure air has been developed of a dispersion vinyl-coated nylon. The cost of the construction is approximately $1.00 per sq ft, which is about one-third the cost of metal prefabs. This type of structure may be a more positive answer to temporary silo facilities to which vinyl and polyethylene may not be the complete answer. Needless to say, the cost of such a structure for silo purposes would be substantially greater at $1.00 a sq ft than vinyl film or sheeting.

U. S. Rubber expects a considerable demand for this type of building will provide needs for temporary storage facilities. The unusual structure before assembly is a 3 x 5-ft package which when expanded is 80 x 40 x 20-ft high. A structure of a weight of 8 ounces per square yard is approximately 10 mils thick. Vinyl-coated nylon panels are sewn to form roof and walls and a tube fabricated of the same material is sewn around the bottom of the structure. Ballast is usually water and serves to fix the building firmly to the flooring. Air pressure inflation is less than 1 psi above atmospheric, and the entire structure can be erected by three men in one hour.

PVC-vinyl acetate copolymer dispersion resins are used in plastisols and organosols for coating of textiles, paper, and metals and are used to a limited extent for the manufacture of foams.

TAPES

Vinyl tapes are important for electrical use because of their high dielectric strength combined with toughness. The high chemical resistance of the tape, abrasion resistance, and ease of application for wire splicing all add to the sale appeal of the items. Vinyls are being used in increasing amounts for surgical tapes and seem to be much superior as a replacement for conventional cotton backing. Certainly a decidedly higher resistance to water wetting is in favor of vinyl compared to the older surgical tapes. Plastisol PVC tape applications are also similarly used with vinyl acetate-vinyl chloride copolymer. The elongation of 200% or higher is another outstanding advantage of vinyl tapes.

The success in Europe of rigid vinyls for pipe applications

under conditions of high acidity have prompted use of vinyl tape as a protective wrapping where pipe must be buried in corrosive soil. Minnesota Mining and Manufacturing Company and Johns-Manville are among the leaders in vinyl tape, as are Johnson & Johnson and Bauer and Black in medical tapes. Pressure-sensitive tapes are a major outlet for vinyl acetate film backings. These tapes can be made in thin gauges, and the sheet or film can be laminated to paper which may or may not be latex impregnated to provide additional strength. Vinylidene chloride-vinyl chloride copolymer (85/15) is also used in thin transparent tape (saran). Johnson & Johnson has added to its "Band-Aid" lines a clear vinyl adhesive bandage. The material is flexible and waterproof. Decorative shoe straps for women are made by extruding vinyl tapes incorporating various fabric and metallic braids.

VINYLIDENE CHLORIDE RESINS

Use of vinylidene chloride polymers is discussed in part in Chapters 1 and 2. Applications were described of copolymers of vinyl chloride and of acrylonitrile for such materials as monofilaments and films. In Table 1.12 (p. 21) volume application is listed in the categories of filament for screening, seat covers and scouring pads, film, paper and other coatings, paint, pipe, staple fiber, and other resins.

Dow Chemical Company produced the first commercial vinylidene chloride polymers in 1940. Shortly after the introduction of saran (85/15 vinylidene chloride/vinyl chloride), some companies began research utilizing vinylidene chloride in a number of copolymerizations. Among the more fruitful studies have been copolymers of acrylonitrile. Saran marketed by Dow can be extruded as monofilament, calendered, and injection, compression or transfer-molded.

The thermal degradation of saran is pronounced, and it is necessary that special metals be used in processing. Among the most accepted is "Hastelloy B." It is also essential that extrusion equipment be designed to permit the minimum possible holdup in the extruder. Extrusion of a formulation can be made utilizing either powder or granules. A general formulation for extrusion of an 85/15 copolymer is:

Resin	100 parts
Plasticizer	4.5 parts
Heat stabilizer	2.0 parts
Light stabilizer	2.0 parts

Dow announced in late 1957 the commercial availability of four ultraviolet light absorbers for use in various resins including halogen-containing polymers. The four materials are: salol (phenyl salicylate), TBS (*tert*-butyl phenyl salicylate), HCB (5-chloro-2-hydroxybenzophenone), and DBR (dibenzoylresorcinol). It is believed that some of these materials, in particular HCB, have been used by Dow for some years in the stabilization of saran. This material is also recommended for the stabilization of vinyl halide formulations. TBS is completely odorless in formulations and has been used in Saran Wrap by Dow for packaging for food wrappings. The odorless, tasteless, nontoxic and nonflammable characteristics of coatings are important advantages in food wrappings.

"Cryovac" and Saran Wrap are effective for vacuum-sealing meats, poultry and cheese products. It is possible that Dow's plasticizer may have been α-methyl benzyl ether. Patent references to the use of tetrachlorophthalate esters as plasticizers have been disclosed. HCB has been an effective light stabilizer and is not as subject to exudation upon orientation as is salol. A number of epoxy compounds are effective heat stabilizers. Extrusion of saran requires the polymer to be heated above its crystallite melting point, at which stage the resin becomes amorphous. The extruded product is of very low strength when cooled and becomes partly crystalline after thorough cooling at room temperature. The oriented polymer develops high tensile strength and greater hardness. Extruded mono-filament has good acceptance in window screening and seat cover applications, while the flat extrusion has use in home scouring pads. Other extrusions have produced tape for wrapping joints and preparation of various materials which require high chemical resistance such as filter cloths, gaskets, valve seats and other articles. Staple fiber has been used in carpets and wool blends. Some application is in articles of wearing apparel such as belts, handbags and shoes. Uphol-stery fabrics for the home, auto and public transportation have been in vogue for years.

The orientation of saran requires the polymer to be uni-formly heated to a temperature above the crystallite melting point and subsequently cooled below this temperature. Orien-tation or stretching effects partial recrystallization of super-cooled polymer and must be carefully controlled by rate of withdrawal in order that the extruded material may be of the desired size and uniformity. Elongation can take place at room temperature, and during this process of mechanical stretching a partial recrystallization occurs, and the crystal-lites are oriented along the major axis of the filament. Subse-quent heat treatment, after or during stretching, can impart the desired degree of crystallization and in turn control prop-erties of the finished polymer which is reeled or packaged. Dow reports that unstretched and unoriented saran has a tensile strength of 8-10,000 psi, is of low impact strength and flexibility.

Stretched and oriented saran, however, has tensile strengths of 30-60,000 psi, a high degree of flexibility, and good impact strength. These stretched and oriented properties are a result of orientation in a single direction with resulting unidirectional properties. The marked crystalline state of vinylidene chloride polymers is most distinct upon examination of x-ray diffrac-tion patterns of oriented crystalline polymer. These desirable properties are particularly useful for small monofilament sections where the load is along the longitudinal axis. Larger sections such as tapes and ovals require transverse orientation which can be imparted by a rolling operation subsequent to quenching. It is logical to believe that Dow has other means of providing transverse orientation.

Interesting data are provided by Dow to illustrate the effect of orientation (elongation) of saran monofilaments versus tensile strength using a stretching time of 5 minutes:

% Total Elongation	Tensile Strength (psi)
0	8,000
100	17,000
150	17,000
200	17,000
250	17,000
300	20,000
350	31,000
400	60,000

Other Vinylidene Chloride Copolymers

Copolymers of vinylidene chloride and vinyl chloride have the greatest sale. However, a number of copolymerizations other than vinyl chloride have been observed for a long time and some of these are commercially in practice.

The literature contains extensive references to copolymerization with acrylonitrile. Other monomers which have been investigated are: vinyl acetate and vinyl crotonate, isobutylene, vinyl methyl ketone, methyl isopropenyl ketone, alkyl methacrylates, vinyl benzoate and chloroprene; also alkyl acrylates, alkyl maleates and fumarates, butadiene, vinyl methyl ketone, allyl chloride, vinyl pyridine, isobutene, and dichlorodifluoroethylene. Dow has recently introduced two vinylidene chloride polymers designated as saran F-220 and saran F-242. Both of these polymers contain acrylonitrile;

the former is believed to have approximately 20% acrylo, the latter 10%. These resins are designed for coatings of various packaging materials which have decreased moisture-vapor transmission, lower gas permeability and increased oil and grease resistance.

Markets are developing for coatings for polyethylene, polyester films and cellophane. The soluble vinylidene chloride-acrylonitrile copolymers are applied using certain ketones, esters, and more powerful solvents such as tetrahydrofuran. As would be expected, copolymers with decreased acrylonitrile have lower solubility than those polymers with higher acrylo contents. Saran F-220 is completely soluble in acetone, but F-242 is insoluble even at elevated temperatures. Table 5.3

TABLE 5.3. PHYSICAL AND FUNCTIONAL PROPERTIES OF SARAN RESIN F-220

Composition	Vinylidene Chloride/ Acrylonitrile Copolymer
Form	White, free flowing powder
Specific gravity	1.60
Refractive index at 25°C.	1.580
Area factor, sq in./lb/mil	17,300
Viscosity, 20% solution in acetone, cps	Approximately 60
Tensile strength, psi	7,000 to 7,500
Per cent elongation	0 to 10
Water vapor transmission (g/100 sq in./24 hr @ 100°F., 90% R.H., 1 mil)	.10
Oxygen transmission (cc/100 sq in./ 24 hr @ 1 atm. pressure difference, 1 mil film @ 23°C.)	0.1
Heat seal range	300 to 350°F.
Grease and oil resistance	Excellent
Chemical resistance	Excellent

describes the physical properties of saran F-220. Solution of vinylidene chloride-acrylonitrile copolymers is best made by agitating the solvent using a high speed stirrer and sifting in the powdered resin. When diluents are employed, agitation is provided, the resin added, and after formation of a slurry the active solvent is added.

Typical vinyl plasticizers may be employed if additional flexibility is desired. Conventional methods of solution coating are used such as dip, reverse and direct roll, and rotogravure. Lacquers may be roller, knife, dip or brush-coated. The three producers of cellophane, American Viscose, duPont and Olin Mathieson all offer polymer-coated cellophane. Printing and heat sealing present no acute problems. Arnold Bakers of Port Chester, New York, have used a modified saran copolymer to coat cellophane and produce a non-fogging material. The non-fogging characteristic in wrapping of bakery products is believed to be due to the deposition of moisture to the inside surface of the coated cellophane as a clear film rather than as droplets characteristic of conventional moisture-proof cellophane.

Vinyl chloride-acrylonitrile copolymer has been used surgically as a replacement for faulty blood vessels. This application is probably of less medical value than "Dacron" and nylon.

Saran 281 is a copolymer of vinylidene chloride and vinyl chloride for molding applications. This material softens at 240-280°F. Sarans have been successfully injection-molded at temperatures of approximately 175°C. and up to 30,000 psi. A number of moldings for the rayon industry have been made due to the stability of the molded parts in chemicals used in processing rayon. Injection molding of saran can produce materials and shapes of desirable properties. As in the case of extrusions, the injection molding machines must be modified only in reference to the metals in contact with the molten polymer. Injection molding of saran utilizes heated dies which in normal sections permit short cycles. The extreme solvent and corrosive resistance of saran has permitted a number of applications where such exposure is serious.

A number of molded items have maximum tensile strengths of 40,000 psi.

Vinylidene and Vinyl Filament and Fibers

Dow Chemical supplies saran to seven processors:

> Firestone Tire & Rubber Company
> Bolta Products
> National Plastics Products Company
> Dawbarn Brothers, Inc.
> Southern Lus-trus Corporation
> The Saran Yarns Company
> Oriented Plastics, Inc.

These manufacturers make filament yarn, staple fiber and tow.

Goodrich, since about 1951, has been developing "Darvan" (formerly Darlan) fiber, a copolymer of vinylidene cyanide and vinyl acetate. Fiber dye acceptance has been a major problem of this cashmere-like fiber.

Vinyl chloride-acetate staple fiber is produced by American Viscose as "Vinyon" in perhaps three million lb a year. Polymers, Inc. has "Bristrand" monofil. PVC fiber which is plasticized is also produced by this firm.

RIGID VINYLS

The early work marking the start of polyvinyl chloride as a commercial material was in 1933 and 1934. Plasticized vinyls have moved rapidly in the United States while rigid development has lagged. Unplasticized PVC has been extensively studied in Germany beginning about 1935 followed by developments in France, Italy and Great Britain, as well as America. Chemical process industries in the European countries required large amounts of rigid PVC due to the metal shortage which developed in Europe during World War II.

British Intelligence Reports estimated rigid production in the Bitterfeld area alone to have been 3500 tons per year in the early years of World War II. It is possible that this breakdown was approximately 1500 tons a year in unplasticized foil and the remaining 2000 tons was for moldings, extrusions and sheet operations. The great shortage of metals in Germany led to utilization of over 1000 tons a year for chemical pipework. Chemical plants in Europe as far back as 1945 were using rigid vinyl pipe 15 inches or more in diameter. It is without dispute that the much more rapid advance of rigid material in Europe is due to a large degree to the enforced search for replacement of metals which were in extremely short supply.

Many types of joints, elbows and nozzles are made of intricate design as well as complicated coil constructions for circulation of corrosive chemicals. Tanks for plating baths have been in vogue for a number of years, as well as hoods and duct work. It is estimated that the total vinyl production in Germany is utilized to an extent of about 20% for rigid applications, while other European countries convert 10-15%.

Perhaps two-thirds of the rigid vinyl in Europe is used for pipes and tubing, and about one-third for sheeting. Much of the tubing is for electrical conduits for both industrial and domestic use, while the U. S. has relied on aluminum. Rigid vinyls could almost be treated in this volume as a "new development," due to the slowness of this progress in the United States. The vast potential of rigid vinyls in America has been cited annually by some people, and finally may be on the verge of fulfillment. The development of low molecular weight polymers of good heat stability has delayed this program somewhat, but it is an inescapable fact that material shortages abroad which were not as critical in America have prompted more rapid development in Europe.

The necessity for design modification of processing equipment is not so acute that extremely radical changes in extruders and the like must be made. More rapid throughput in rigid fabrications coupled with good quality would certainly help promote this industry. It is believed entirely possible that major improvements in design of extruders for rigid vinyls will more likely provide a major production break-through than will the already significant contribution of lower molecular weight polymers on the part of the resin manufacturer.

The most outstanding property of rigid PVC is chemical inertness. Combined with this inertness is excellent weathering properties. Rigid vinyl is attractive because it is light in weight, will not support combustion, has good electrical resistivity, chemical resistance, unaffected by moisture, and can be processed to produce clear, translucent or opaque articles of good strength. Rigid Type I PVC has exceptional chemical resistance and adequate heat distortion temperature and impact strength. The impact strength (Izod) of 0.4-1 ft-lb/in. notch is materially increased to 15 ft-lb or more (Type II) by blending the vinyl with styrene-acrylonitrile or butadiene-acrylonitrile copolymer or a styrene-acrylonitrile-butadiene polymer.

The use of rigid vinyls in water pipes appears to be possible at temperatures normally used to convey hot water in the home. Although hot water is not normally so piped today, it may be in the future. Vinyl water pipe imparts no taste, odor or toxicity. Flanges, T's, and elbows are now being produced by injection molding of rigids.

Rigid vinyls incorporating a stabilizer and lubricant only can be milled, calendered, extruded, molded in various operations, machined and welded. The vinyl resin manufacturer and the fabricator share certain problems in rigid development. The hot-melt plasticity of unplasticized polymer must be balanced against thermal stability. Coupled with these concepts is the softening temperature of the resin. Strides have been made in the polymer manufacturing industries, and low molecular weight vinyl chloride homopolymer of good plastic flow and entirely adequate heat stability can now be obtained. The impact strength and heat distortion temperature (particularly the latter) of low and high molecular weight PVC are not sufficiently different to be of undue concern to most fabricators. As the molecular weight of a series of PVC increases, heat distortion temperature increases only slightly, while impact resistance shows significantly higher values.

The following data illustrate two series of PVC resins manufactured by Escambia Chemical. For some processors type 1200 resin rather than type 1225 would be used due to its lower average molecular weight enabling lower processing temperatures and greater plastic flow.

Escambia PVC Type	Specific Viscosity (ASTM)	Heat Distortion, °C. (ASTM)		Izod Impact Strength ft-lb/in.	Plasticity * sq mm
		66 psi	264 psi		
1185	0.27	80	72	0.47	2235
1200	0.31	79	70	0.58	1915
1225	0.37	80	71	0.75	1765
2185	0.27	78	72	0.55	2250
2200	0.31	80	75	0.76	1880
2225	0.37	80	75	0.75	1660

* Area in sq mm of 1 gm polymer pressed at 400°F.

It is unmistakably true that as the specific viscosity increases, the plastic flow decreases. One must therefore balance the desire to obtain somewhat better physical properties against ease of processing. It is generally found that an increase in the degree of polymerization does not give greatly significant improvement in heat distortion temperature.

Copolymerization of vinyl acetate with vinyl chloride results in a decrease in heat distortion temperature with an increase in the percentage of the comonomer, although plasticity increases as the percent of comonomer increases. The effect of comonomer on impact strength is not as clear-cut.

TABLE 5.4. PHYSICAL PROP|

	ASTM	Vinyl Chloride Acetate Copolymer	Type I Vinyl Chloride	Type II Vinyl Chloride	Vinyli Chlor
Specific gravity	792-47T	1.38	1.32-1.40	1.35	1.70
Tensile strength, psi	638-49T	7,000-8,500	7,000-9,000	2,000-6,000	7,000-8,
Flexural strength, psi	790-49T	14,500	14,500	12,000	5,000
Izod impact, ft lb/in. of notch @ 72°F.	256-47T	0.5	0.4-1.0	15-20	0.3-7.0
Thermal expansion /°C. $\times 10^{-5}$	696-47T	7	5-7	10	19
Heat Distortion, °F. @ 264 psi	648-45T	145	140-175	155-185	140
Moisture absorption, % 24 hr	570-42	negligible	negligible	negligible	negligit
Water vapor permeability g/100 sq in./24 hr *	E96-53T	0.5 (5 mil)	0.7 (5 mil)	7-10	0.2 (1 n
Rockwell Hardness	785-48T	105 "R"	120 "R"	90-118 "R"	50 "M"
Flammability, in./min.	D635	Self Ext.	Self Ext.	Self Ext.	Self Ex

* Moisture-proof cellophane 0.2-1.0

One often observes that either vinyl acetate or vinylidene chloride copolymerized with vinyl chloride will show higher impact strengths up to perhaps 10% by weight of the comonomer. Percentages of comonomer higher than this rapidly result in decreased impact strength. The increase in plasticity due to copolymerization is no more pronounced than is the decrease in heat distortion temperature which occurs as a more or less straight-line function with increase in percent of the comonomer.

Studies in this laboratory on PVC have substantiated the work of Walter in 1954, who found that a VYNW/DOP composition indicated that the Young's Modulus obtained by unidirectional compression measurements passes through a

RIGID THERMOPLASTIC SHEET

Poly- thylene	Poly- styrene	High Impact Poly- styrene	Modified Styrene- acrylo- Nitrile	Poly- methyl Metha- crylate	Ethyl Cellulose	Cellulose Acetate	Cellulose Acetate- Butyrate
	1.05	1.05	1.06	1.18	1.14-1.16	1.25-1.35	1.18
)-2,500	7,000	3,000	4,000	9,000	6,000-10,000	9,000	6,500
	10,000	6,000	6,000	16,000	6,000	6,000	6,000
	0.25	0.8	8	0.4	1.5	1.0	2-6
	6	8	10	9	15	12	15
	180	165	170	175	130	140	145
gible	negligible	0.1	0.5	0.3	1.2	4.0	1.6
(1 mil)	—	6.0	—	—	20-50	—	60 (1 mil)
R"	120 "R"	100 "R"	75 "R"	90 "M"	110 "R"	105 "R"	104 "R"
	2.0	2.0	3.0	0.5-2.5	1.0	7.0	1.0

See tensile strength as function of orientation—Chapter 5

maximum at about 10% DOP content. Work at Escambia has shown that lightly plasticized stock has markedly decreased Izod impact strength. Studies by Weldon in England substantiate these observations. Weldon has also shown that as little as 5% DOP will decrease the softening temperature as much as 18°C.

Rigid Sheeting

The total volume of thermoplastic sheeting for vinyl polymer and copolymer, cellulosics, styrene and acrylics was approximately 2 million lb in 1951 and 50 million lb in 1954. The estimated 1957 market was 225-250 million lb, of which perhaps 15-20 million was rigid vinyl sheeting. The growth possibility of rigid sheeting exists, but this too has not met the prediction of the enthusiastic forecasts. One can point to the steel industry, as well as the aluminum industry, which utilizes perhaps 30-40% of their total production in the form of sheet as potential goals of plastic sheeting. The rigid vinyl industry has replaced a very small portion of the metallic sheet to date.

Certainly plastics will never replace the metals to a majority extent. Rigid PVC and vinyl chloride-vinyl acetate copolymer have experienced growth in sheeting application, but cellulosics, polystyrene and polymethyl methacrylate are all sold in greater volume. The physical properties of rigid thermoplastic sheet are described in Table 5.4. Polymers included in this compilation are vinyl chloride-acetate copolymer, Type I and Type II vinyls, vinylidene chloride, polyethylene, polystyrene and high impact polystyrene, styrene-acrylonitrile, polymethyl methacrylate, ethyl cellulose, cellulose acetate, and cellulose acetate butyrate. A large proportion of rigid vinyl sheeting is manufactured of vinyl chloride-vinyl acetate copolymer. A comparison of the physical properties of Types I and II versus polyethylene is of interest. In Chapter 2 a general description of these materials is given. Table 2.15 lists the properties of flexible versus rigid PVC. The physical characteristics of the rigids and chemical resistance are also described.

Type I PVC can be described as possessing excellent chemical resistance combined with normal impact strength, the highest tensile strength of thermoplastic pipes, good dimensional stability and weathering properties, resistance to creep, and the ability to be used over a wide temperature range. The outstanding disadvantages are the limitations of temperature and pressure and greater weight than polyethylene. Outstanding uses are many although perhaps its high chemical resistance makes process piping one of its major potential applications. Type I PVC can also be used for duct work requiring anti-corrosive properties, conveying salt water, and sour crude oil.

(*Courtesy Escambia Chemical Corporation*)

Figure 5.11. Experimental calendering of rigid vinyl sheet.

Type II (high impact) like Type I has flame resistance, dimensional stability, toughness, and vastly improved impact strength. Although the chemical resistance of the high-impact product is good, it is considerably inferior to unmodified PVC. Another disadvantage of Type II is its lower resistance to oxidizing agents. Both types in general have the same uses with the exception of applications involving extremely high chemical resistance. Where shock characteristics are especially desired, the modified resin is most prominent. The two types are joined by solvent cementing with slip sleeve fittings, by hot welding and by threading.

The total sale of plastic pipe in 1957 is estimated at about 70 million dollars at retail price levels and was 55 million dollars in 1956. *Plumbing and Heating Business* for May, 1957, states that the biggest single use for plastic pipe is in jet pump installations and other rural water system piping. Irrigation and sprinkling systems also have good growth prospect, while cold water lines are believed by this journal to be the greatest single use for plastic pipe for some years to come. Some think that the total plastic pipe industry will show several times or more sale in 1960 over that of 1957. Saran piping has been used for many years, and perhaps its only limitation has been the use of a few parts of plasticizer which causes ultimate enbrittlement. Saran has been used to line steel pipe. Polyethylene plastic pipe represents perhaps 70% or more of the total United States market. The new high density polyethylene is rigid unlike the earlier low density material, and this should make the high density material more attractive in some applications.

The U. S. Navy's choice of PVC for complete ship washdown systems for spraying sea water to remove radioactive contamination is a major indication of the versatility of PVC. Data compiled by Nixon Nitration Works state that on the basis of 0.020-in. thicknesses for comparison of rigid sheeting the cost of modified styrene is $.065 per sq ft, rigid vinyl $.089, cellulose acetate $.125 and cellulose acetate butyrate $.136. The vinyls were stated to have advantages over their competition due to ease of forming, dimensional stability, and greater rigidity. This company believes that present and potential large volume markets for rigid vinyl lie in fields of laminating, decorative materials, graphic arts, business machines and credit cards and as wall covering.

Thermoplastic rigid sheets have major potential in the packaging field for use in contoured, bubble and skin packs, and various containers and dispensing articles. Rigid vinyl perhaps represents something less than 10% of the total sale of rigid thermoplastic sheet. It is debatable whether vinyl will acquire a greater portion of this market in the near future, although the possibility does exist.

A calendered rigid PVC is produced by Anorgana in Germany. The material is offered in thicknesses from 0.0012 to 0.012 in. in rolls 26 in. wide with one surface coated for heat sealing between 80-110°C. The coated surface will seal to the uncoated and the unplasticized film will adhere to many plastic films or sheeting and to fabrics. A transparent vinyl "can" is made of calendered, clear, 8 mil PVC sheet which is unplasticized and reputedly nontoxic. The body of the package is formed from roll stock by a stamping machine and the vinyl cover is vacuum-formed, and a died-out, crimp-on metal sealing ring is provided.

The plastic combines good strength, low water vapor transmission rate and a high resistance to greases and oils. Application is for a packaging container for fish and margarine. Anorgana states the film or sheet can be drawn half its diameter or more. Price in Germany is 68 cents for 8-mil film and 65 cents for 12-mil sheeting. The film can also be used for the production of bottles from a single piece. Blown rigid vinyl has been produced on a limited basis in the United States, but it is doubtful whether it is now commercially produced. Some application of rigid vinyl film is for European vacuum-forming operations to manufacture cups or containers whose primary use is ice cream and milk cartons.

Rigid vinyl sheeting for lining auto interiors is scuff-resistant and of pleasing appearance. Adhesives can be used to provide a laminate of vinyl sheeting to a fiberboard base. It is perhaps the major material used in the manufacture of credit cards due to ease of printing, embossing and die cutting. Another use is to protect against injury due to solvents and chemicals splashing on personnel. Vinyl outerwear serves a similar purpose as semi-flexible material for face pieces.

Sheeting is making progress in both daylight and artificial lighting and is being used in over-all ceiling illumination. Excellent light diffusion and uniformity results. The transparent sheets are formed for the particular installation and are being most often used when combined with fluorescent fixtures. Plexall Corporation has constructed a rigid display case of 25 gauge sheeting utilizing electric bonding techniques.

Electric Storage Battery Company uses braided glass-lined rigid PVC sleeves in manufacture of truck batteries of exceptionally long life. Calendered sheeting permits reduction in wall thickness, and its chemical resistance gives longer service life than rubber or polyethylene.

Rigid Pipe and Profiles

Extrusion of Type I and Type II vinyls, while still of small volume, is awakening greater interest. Germany has used Type I pipe quite extensively since about 1935 for conveying cold water and for many applications in chemical plants. The use in America is relatively new, and as yet its consumption is very much less than that of polyethylene. Low-density polyethylene had low rigidity and low working pressures, which may be overcome by the newer high-density material. Oil-field utilization of polyethylene is somewhat restricted by the deposition of paraffinic hydrocarbons in the pipe, which choke off the effective transporting area. The low softening temperature of polyethylene, flammable properties, low abrasion resistance, attack by petroleum hydrocarbons, and ultraviolet light attack all make polyethylene pipe somewhat vulnerable to polyvinyl chloride. In today's market PVC has higher cost than polyethylene, and it too is not resistant to some organic solvents, although its chemical resistance is substantially greater than that of polyethylene. High temperature and pressure limitations, as in polyethylene, are imposed on PVC. The major difficulty which has faced the vinyl pipe industry is the difficulty in extrusion, which perhaps outweighs all other disadvantages. Much technical progress has been made.

Vinylidene chloride was the first plastic pipe in volume use in America. Use of this polymer is becoming increasingly restricted to linings for metal pipe, as some of its earlier applications have yielded to PVC. The cost of PVC pipe is still approximately half again as much as that of polyethylene and in turn somewhat less than that of vinylidene chloride. The tensile strength and working pressure of PVC are substantially higher than those of polyethylene (see Table 5.4).

There is as yet no plastic or metal pipe whose chemical resistance is such that its use can be universal. Perhaps the materials of greatest chemical resistance are PVC and vinylidene chloride whose general chemical resistance is superior to that of copper, brass, cast iron and carbon steel, though somewhat less than that of stainless steel.

Monsanto has estimated that sales of plastic material for pipe application will be 75 million lb in 1960, and 300 million lb by 1975. Sales of plastic pipe for 1957 are estimated at 40 million dollars. Applications of greatest potential promise appear to lie in the petroleum industry, homes, agricultural uses, chemical process industries, sewerage and waste disposal and in utilities. The use of pipe of all types in homes is estimated to be 525 million lb per year. Vinyl pipe may conceivably share this market, particularly if the material can be used for hot water piping. The vinyls may substantially replace metal in piping cold water in homes in the next ten years.

One of the factors which has delayed vinyl pipe development in America has been the necessity for improving not only fabrication of the pipe but ease of installation. National Tube Division of U. S. Steel, the world's largest supplier of pipe, started distribution of PVC pipe in 1955. The improvement in laying pipe was clearly demonstrated in late 1955 when an inexperienced crew laid 2800 feet of 2-in. line in

1¾ hours. This installation of National Tube's pipe was at a Texas oil field and involved the coupling of 90 lengths of Type I PVC at the rate of almost a joint per minute. National Tube utilizes both normal and high impact pipe and fittings for the usual steel pipe types, plus additional ones which permit entire assemblies to be manufactured of vinyl. The fittings are made by Tube Turns Plastics. Pipe is produced with both plain or threaded ends.

The installation described above used plain end pipe which was first cleaned with a volatile material. The dried pipe and socket were coated with solvent cement, and the couplings engaged and rotated 90° to establish firm contact. Carbon tetrachloride, or a less toxic solvent, can be used to clean the fittings. PVC pipe can also be joined by welding with heat or by adhesives. Solvent cementing requires up to two days to develop full strength of the bond. National Tube and others do not consider such installation a novelty, but an application of the best possible material for the job. Metal pipes are also being wrapped with flexible and semi-flexible vinyl "tapes" to decrease the corrosion rate of the metal when buried in corrosive soil, the attack of which is particularly severe in oil fields. The installation of vinyl pipe is perhaps four times as rapid as for metal. This helps offset the higher cost of vinyl versus steel, and in some cases permits installed cost of the vinyls to be equivalent to a steel pipe installation.

The cost of vinyl pipe will be lowered when extrusion engineering design will permit greater extrusion rates. These rates today are one-third to one-half that of polyethylene, and less than 1% of the rate of steel pipe. Another severe limitation has been restricted use in many thermal applications and high-pressure requirements. Vinyl pipe can successfully compete today in cost versus copper and alloy pipe. The lower extrusion rates compared with steel are considerably offset by the much lower capital investment required for extruding vinyl pipe. The petroleum industry appears to have the largest application potential for this resin in pipe in 1965, and perhaps will be followed in consumption by gas and water, utilities, chemical industries, agricultural and mining. It is predicted that the plastic pipe monopoly of polyethylene will yield at least in part to the vinyls. Pipe up to 15 in. in diameter and 20 ft in length is known to be manufactured. The weight of vinyl pipe is attractive: 3-in. pipe Schedule 40, 80 and 120 weighs 133, 180 and 207 lb, respectively, per 100 ft. Rigid pipe can be cut with any ordinary saw and threaded on standard metal pipe-threading equipment. The pipe can be conveniently heated and bent if necessary. A cost comparison of pipe and fittings versus brass and copper are in Table 5.5.

TABLE 5.5. RIGID VINYL PIPE AND FITTINGS COST COMPARISON PER 100'

Schedule 40 Red Brass Pipe over 2000 ft or lb		Copper Pipe	Copper Tubing Type K, .134 wall	Copper Tubing Type L, .110 wall	PVC Schedule 40 Type I and II	PVC Schedule 80 Type I and II
2″	$220.51	$225.07	$122.04	$110.34	$ 99.00	$133.00
3″	458.17	466.68	229.38	197.30	196.00	265.00
4″	706.97	714.11	385.71	328.99	279.00	388.00
6″			929.43	701.44	471.00	709.00

Fittings	Brass Screw 90° L	T		PVC 90° L	T
2″	$ 2.52	$ 3.50		$ 2.56	$ 2.96
3″	7.38	9.31		9.16	14.40
4″	17.17	23.28		13.69	21.61

Valves	Gate
2″	$ 17.26
3″	41.61
4″	152.00

Rigid fittings can be obtained in tees, couplings, 45° and 90° elbows, reducing bushings, unions, threaded flanges and plugs. Rigid diaphragm and plug valves can be made for use with corrosive materials and slurries at temperatures up to 150°F. and pressures to 150 lb. These valves are easy to open and shut, have superior chemical resistance to most materials, and require little maintenance needs.

In transporting water no taste or odor is imparted, and the material is approved by the National Sanitation Foundation for use in potable drinking water systems. The U. S. Department of Agriculture has also given approval for rigid vinyl pipe to convey brine in meat packing plants. Flow rates up to 25% greater than metal pipe of comparable size are obtained. High abrasion resistance permits conveying slurries which would scratch many metals and plastics, including polyethylene. The fire resistance particularly favors PVC over polyethylene, while its corrosion resistance in contact with many materials is also vastly superior. The vinyl has the best outdoor aging properties of any available thermoplastic material.

Vinyl cores are used in steel cable by Jones and Laughlin to provide resiliency for the steel when used in drilling operations. Similar items of semi-rigid and rigid vinyls are used in conjunction with wire and cable.

Rigid piping is known to be used in the following industries and processes:

Home and municipal water	Irrigation
Agriculture	Bleach
Oil fields	Municipal waste treatment
Chemical equipment	Chemical plants
Steel mills	Vent pipes
Pulp and paper mills	Electroplating
Rayon	Power plants
Meat packing	Deionizer equipment
Mining	Conveying sulfuric acid
Atomic energy	Leather tanning
Food and beverage	Paint manufacture
Pharmaceutical	Soap manufacture
Gas and oil	Photography

Brine and salt water	Wine and vinegar manufacture
Pipe	Automotive
Atomic wash-down	Aviation
	Battery manufacture

Rigid vinyl pipe can only improve in sales volume due to its still relatively small position. It is believed that its many assets will ultimately make this use one of its major sales aspects.

High-impact material has been used in underground sprinkler assemblies. San Antonio, Texas, installed 25,000 ft of the material in 1956, which has been under 70 lb constant static pressure without a single pipe failure.

A study of plastic pipe for potable water supply was made by the National Sanitation Foundation and sponsored by the Society of the Plastics Industry. Twenty-two different samples of plastic pipe were studied, and the results were published in 1956. The resins included polyethylene, PVC, saran, rubber-modified polystyrene, and cellulose acetate butyrate. These findings show that all samples weathered for one year with slight changes. Soil burial in an acid soil of pH 2.0 at 35°C. for one year with intermittent wetting and drying showed little effect on any of the plastics. Copper pipe, however, was considerably oxidized, while galvanized steel showed pronounced deterioration. Prolonged submersion in water resulted in little change of any of the materials. Taste and odor characteristics of the transported water were acceptable. Controlled feeding studies of rats drinking of the plastic systems showed no deviation from the findings of control specimens.

Profile Extrusion

The high tensile and flexural strength of the vinyls make profile extrusions particularly attractive. The physical characteristics of pipe and tubing applications are also of more than passing interest in profile extrusions. The outstanding outdoor aging properties give the resin an edge over competitive plastic materials in many applications. The flame resistance of both Type I and Type II rigids is substantially better than the very poor polyethylene, polystyrene, ethyl cellulose, styrene-acrylonitrile copolymer and cellulose acetate butyrate. Rigid insulators in the electrical industry are used for metal contact conductors for overhead power lifts. This appears to be an application of growth. Housings for a number of articles of equipment are made. Strips for refrigerators are now an important item. Edgings for ceramic tile and many types of channeling for the manufacturing industry, including automotive, have been fabricated.

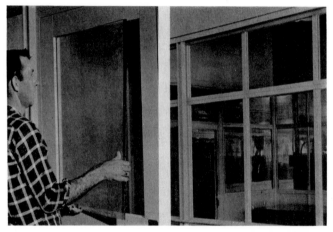

(*Courtesy Bakelite Company*)

Figure 5.12. Laminate of rigid vinyl sheet for industrial windows.

Additional applications of rigid PVC which have good growth prospects are in electrical conduits and duct work, casement window frames, desk edging, home appliance trim strips, automotive moldings and trim and sliding door runners. Considerable potential for Type II material is in casement and storm window sash and track. Corrosion resistant ducts and tanks are currently the biggest outlet of rigid vinyls (Type I).

Vinylidene chloride polymer is believed to have limited growth prospect in pipe.

Compound Preparation

Rigid vinyls can be compounded with little change in formulation for milling, calendering, extrusion, compression and injection molding, and deep-drawing and vacuum-forming operations. Compounds can be extruded and molded from both powder mixes and granular materials. Most of the extrusions in the United States use granular material, but the success of European operations with powder blends give evidence that this method will someday be predominant in the United States.

Many stabilizers have been used in rigid processing, and it is believed by some manufacturers that basic lead carbonate is perhaps the most effective. Other processors of rigids prefer organo-tins or barium-cadmium soaps. Alkaline-earth compounds are frequently supplemented by epoxies. The wire and cable industry prefers lead stabilizers to all other types. Other lead products such as lead stearate are used as a lubricant. In some cases minor amounts of plasticizer of 2 to 5% or so are incorporated to decrease the processing temperature with a resulting decrease in decomposition, improve plastic flow and to lessen brittleness of the end product.

A popular lubricant is calcium stearate; however, it has been found that reduced impact strength can result from its use. Waxes and titanium dioxide are usually incorporated to the extent of about 2 parts each, although as much as 20 parts of the latter has been used.

Escambia has extruded both Type I and II from powder blends, although to date lower than normal impact strength results from the latter extrusion. To 100 parts of medium to low molecular weight resin (Escambia PVC 1225 and 1200;

ASTM specific viscosity 0.37 and 0.31, resp.) are added 2-3 parts of a stabilizer (often "Thermolite"-31) and 0.5 part of a lubricant. The compound can be internally mixed and milled not unlike previously described operations. A procedure sometimes followed is to dry mix all ingredients and charge the material to a warm internal mixer. A short mixing cycle is employed and the stock removed prior to fluxing, milled at 350°F. stock temperature, and sheeted. The sheeting can be calendered at 330°F. or higher. Extrusions of pelletized material have been made at 15-20 rpm, with no screen packing, but high production demands use of a breaker plate and screen packs. Rigid extrusions generally require conditions somewhat comparable to those described for the extrusion of vinylidene chloride copolymers (saran). Careful operation of take up units must be maintained to obtain products of the proper dimension and appearance. Extrusion of Type I PVC from powder mixes does require breaker plate and screen packs to give stock temperature of approximately 350°F.

The incorporation of a rubber acts as an extrusion aid and markedly improves the flow characteristics not only in extrusions but in calendering and injection-molding operations (Type II). Type II resin-rubber blends are gaining in popularity and excellent sale is predicted by 1960. In early days of high-impact compounds, latex blending of the soft butadiene/acrylonitrile and styrene/acrylonitrile resins (often called rubbers) was in vogue. The rubber latex was blended with either a PVC latex or PVC powder prepared by suspension or emulsion methods. The latex was coagulated or spray-dried, followed by milling of compound and dicing if extruded. The N-type rubbers can also be polymers of butadiene-styrene-acrylonitrile. One of the more outstanding materials is "Cycolac," manufactured by Marbon Chemical. In most operations the "rubber" is mixed with medium to low molecular weight PVC containing stabilizers, lubricants, fillers on occasion and antioxidants, if sufficient is not included in the rubber compound. The type of resin (or rubber) added to the PVC can be varied to satisfy the particular requirements of calendering, extrusion, and molding. To date these Type II operations have required pelletized and not powder blend compound.

TABLE 5.6. PROCESSING CONDITIONS RIGID (TYPE II) PELLETIZED COMPOUND. TECHNICAL SERVICE LABORATORY-ESCAMBIA CHEMICAL CORPORATION

Extrusion

Machine 2½″ National Rubber Machinery	
Barrel Temp. (°F.)	
Zone 1	320
” 2	330
” 3	340
” 4	350
Head temp.	360
Gate	360
Die	350
Stock	360
Screw water	52
Hopper water	52
Power, amps	22
Screw speed, rpm	11
Breaker plate	none-2
Screens, mesh	20
* * *	
Izod impact (ft lb/in.)	15.0
Heat distortion (°C.)	
@ 66 psi stress	83
@ 264 psi stress	77

Calender

Mill	
Stock temp. (°F.)	370
Roll temp.	340
Calender	
Offset (°F.)	320
Top	320
Middle	330
Bottom	340

Injection Molding

Machine Reed-Prentice, 4-6 oz	
Cylinder temp. (°F.)	
Front	360
Center	350
Rear	340
Ram pressure (psig)	20,000
Holding pressure (psig)	18,000
Plunger forward (sec.)	35
Dies closed (sec.)	45
Delayed unload (sec.)	30
Dies open (sec.)	10
Mold temp. (°F.)	180
* * *	
Hardness (Rockwell R)	95
Izod impact (ft lb/in.)	16.75
Heat distortion (°C.)	
@ 66 psi stress	84
@ 264 psi stress	74

Laminates of calendered sheets are compression-molded up to 1-inch thickness or more. Compression-molded rigids must be molded at sufficiently high temperatures to generate maximum tensile strength. This fact must be balanced against the increased thermal decomposition occurring at these higher processing temperatures. Incorporation of suitable rubbers with PVC of good plastic flow can produce injection-molded articles of fine quality. The pressure required for such an operation is often 20,000 psi, and even higher pressures are sometimes recommended. Rigid pipe fittings are an outstanding development. (See Table 5.6 for Type II extrusion, calendering and injection molding conditions).

Deep drawing or vacuum forming is a small-volume application to date. A workable sheet temperature is 275°F. for Types I and II. One of the largest applications of rigid vacuum forming has been by the military for production of dimensionally stable three-dimensional maps. Advertising window displays use 20-mil sheeting. Plaques and figures are also vacuum-formed from pre-printed or lithograph sheets of 10-mil sheeting using molds cast from epoxy resin. Vacuum-forming for tile applications is a promising outlet. Seiberling Rubber Company and Kaye-Tex manufacture rigid sheet for such purposes. Seiberling also produces rigid to be used as a nose guard for application as an air scoop cover for jet fighter planes of North American Aviation. These vacuum-formed covers prohibit foreign objects from entering the jet engines of the planes during storage and delivery. Ceiling panels of vinyl are excellent for indirect lighting application.

The electrical properties of the vinyls create a problem of static electricity. A number of patents deal with the use of various additives which will reduce or prevent the static charge. Perhaps the best of these materials are non-ionic surface active materials of polyalkylene glycol types. Static problems exist in rigids and flexibles.

GENERAL

To date the incorporation of vinyl chloride polymer with styrene has been most limited. However, some degree of emphasis is currently being placed on the preparation of flame-resistant sheeting composed of the two ingredients. Little is known about this material at the present, but it has been reported that Izod impact strengths as high as 10 ft-lb/in. at room temperature have been obtained.

Vinyl tubes have limited use in the packaging industry. Open end tubes when filled can be readily heat sealed. Some oil paints are being packaged of this material.

The higher vinyl fatty acid esters are effective viscosity index stabilizers for lubricating oils.

6. NEW DEVELOPMENTS

All manufacturers of vinyls in the United States were solicited by letter for new developments now in production or in the near or foreseeable future. The response has not been great. It is of course obvious that application developments are increasing at a rapid rate, while new vinyl polymers and methods of polymerization occur most infrequently. Escambia's basically new PVC "Pearl" polymer is therefore presented. This development was first presented at the 14th Annual Technical Conference of the Society of Plastics Engineers in Detroit in January, 1958.

PVC Pearls

A new process for the polymerization of vinyl chloride was developed. This process yields a polymer having a large, uniform particle size. The polymer is completely dust-free. The polymer particles resemble white porous pearls, and the new product is called Escambia "Pearl" PVC®. Four grades of the Pearl PVC are commercially available: types 2250, 2225, 2200 and 2185 representing high, medium, low and very low molecular weight, respectively.

A comparison of the PVC Pearl polymer with conventional vinyl chloride polymers has been made. Vinyl chloride is usually polymerized by most manufacturers either as an emulsion or a suspension in water. In an emulsion polymerization, relatively large amounts of surface-active agents and catalysts are used. The resulting emulsion is then spray-dried or flocculated and a polymer having a very small particle size is obtained. Most of the polymerization additives remain occluded to the polymer. The presence of these residual catalyst fragments and surface-active agents in the finished polymer is not always deleterious. However, in applications which require superior color, clarity, heat resistance and electrical properties these added materials cannot be tolerated.

Most suspension polymerization formulations yield resins which contain minimum amounts of additives. In this process the amount of surface-active agents is very low, and the resulting polymeric product is obtained as a suspension which is separated from the water by filtration or centrifugation. The suspension process usually produces a polymer having a broad particle size distribution, ranging from dust-like particles of several microns to large particles of several hundred microns. However, as there is little extraneous matter present, the color, clarity, heat resistance and electrical properties are good.

In the production of polyvinyl chloride by the suspension process, an attempt is frequently made to produce a small particle size. In most, but not all, suspension PVC polymerizations, the best processing and physical properties are obtained with a small particle size resin. However, this makes handling more difficult and results in losses due to dust.

Polyvinyl chloride produced by the Pearl process has a very large particle size. In addition, this resin has been found to process more easily than the other suspension resins. The physical properties of finished Pearl compounds are equal or superior to those of conventional resins. Some of the most important processing characteristics and physical properties will be described in detail.

Particle Size. The Pearl polymers are characterized by an unusually large, uniform particle size. A comparison of the particle size as determined by screen analysis of a PVC Pearl polymer with two widely accepted commercial PVC resins which were probably prepared by suspension processes is shown in Table 6.1. The absence of very small particles or fines in the Pearl polymer eliminates such problems as dust and reduces material loss in storage and processing.

TABLE 6.1. PARTICLE SIZE: PVC PEARLS AND CONVENTIONAL VINYL RESINS

Screen Analysis % Retained on	PVC Pearls Type 2250	Resin A	Resin B
20 Mesh screen	0	0	0
40 Mesh screen	21	0	1
80 Mesh screen	79	26	3
100 Mesh screen	0	54	20
140 Mesh screen	0	17	47
200 Mesh screen	0	3	20
Through 200 mesh	0	0	9
Bulk density (lb/cu ft)	30.2	30.6	33.2
Relative viscosity (1% in cyclohexanone @ 25°C.)	2.45	2.37	2.44

While the particle size is large, the bulk density is found to be similar to that of conventional suspension resins. While the absence of dust is important, the other desirable properties of this resin are more so.

The Pearl particles appear to be smooth, uniform spheres when examined without magnification. However, photomicrographs have shown that they actually have a rough, pitted surface. Thus, while the size is large, the effective surface area is also large, due to the microscopic irregularity of the particles. This is confirmed by absorption studies.

In Figure 6.1, a photomicrograph (66 X) of the Pearl polymer is compared with one of a suspension polymer. The large particle size, uniformity, and the absence of dust are evident. The surface roughness indicates that the particles are quite porous.

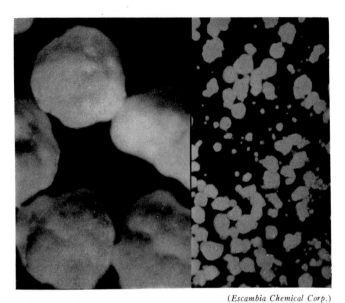

(*Escambia Chemical Corp.*)

PVC Pearls   Resin A

Figure 6.1.

Plasticizer Absorption. A great deal of the polyvinyl chloride resin produced is used in applications which require a flexible material. This flexibility is achieved by the incorporation of suitable plasticizers. It is frequently convenient to pre-blend the resin and the plasticizer. The mixture is then heated below the fusion temperature of the resin and a dry blend should be obtained.

An acceptable PVC resin is capable of absorbing the required amount of plasticizer and yielding a dry blend on heating. The dry blend must also possess sufficient dryness to flow through lines or be blown through a conveying system without caking or otherwise interfering with the processing operation.

It is generally accepted that dry blending for extrusion applications can be varied to make product of the very finest quality or material which upon extrusion will be totally rejected due to excessive gel count. Naturally, conditions of dry blending cannot be firmly stated for any type of PVC because such variables as type of dry blend equipment to be used, temperature to be employed, quantity and type of plasticizers, stabilizers, fillers, lubricants, etc., all must be considered for the specific purpose and application in mind. The Escambia Pearl resin has a most unusual property of producing dry blends which are free-flowing with up to 120 parts of DOP. This great absorptive capacity of the Pearls in many applications of dry blending can best be performed by initially adding the plasticizer at room temperature to the resin also at room temperature. This permits use of plasticizer at low levels to be evenly distributed and not overly plasticize some particles and underplasticize others. Use of 50 parts DOP for many applications can therefore be best done by room temperature dry blending of the ingredients followed by heating to 220°F. or higher to produce a dry blend of exceptional flow properties.

The heating time required to produce resin-plasticizer dry blends and the flow properties of these blends were studied. The resin and plasticizer were blended in a Hobart Mixer (model N-50). A steam jacket was built on the bowl of this mixer and the temperature of the bowl was held at 100°C. during the test. The mixer was operated at the #1 (slowest) speed. The dry blend time is defined as the time required to produce a dry resin-plasticizer mixture while the bowl is held at this temperature. A comparison of the dry blend times of the PVC Pearl polymer with two commercial resins reported to have outstanding dry blend qualities was made and is shown in Table 6.2 and Figure 6.2. The PVC Pearl resin is about equivalent to the best commercial resins in its ability to quickly absorb 50 parts of dioctyl phthalate per 100 parts of polymer. However, only the Pearl polymer would absorb 100 parts of dioctyl phthalate and yield a dry blend in this test. The Pearls are therefore strongly recommended where high plasticizer levels are used.

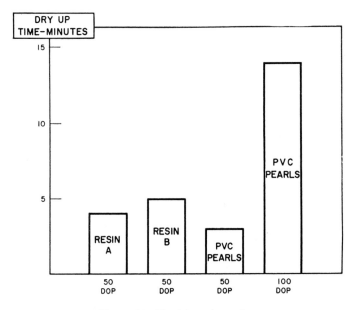

Figure 6.2. Plasticizer absorption.

For maximum processing economy, not only should a resin have good plasticizer absorption, but the resulting dry blends must flow readily. The flow times of resin-plasticizer blends through a 60° stainless steel funnel having a one-half inch opening were measured. In Figure 6.3, these flow rates of PVC Pearls-dioctyl phthalate dry blends are shown to be

TABLE 6.2. ABSORPTION OF DIOCTYL PHTHALATE PLASTICIZER
BY PVC RESINS

Resin	Parts DOP Per Hundred Resin	Dry Up Time—Min.	Dry Blend Flow Rate g/sec.
PVC Pearls	—	—	9.1
PVC Pearls	30	0	8.4
PVC Pearls	50	3	6.2
PVC Pearls	70	5	4.5
PVC Pearls	90	11	4.4
PVC Pearls	100	14	4.0
PVC Pearls	120	85	3.8
PVC Pearls	150	180	3.4
A	—	—	7.7
A	30	1	6.7
A	50	4	3.2
A	70	5	2.9
A	90	15	2.3
A	100	100+	Will not flow
B	—	—	5.0
B	30	5	Will not flow
B	50	5	Will not flow

high, even at extremely high plasticizer levels. One of the conventional resins is seen to flow fairly well at moderate dioctyl phthalate levels, but the other fails to flow even at the low dioctyl phthalate level. Only the Pearl polymer produces dry blends with high and relatively constant flow rates over wide dioctyl phthalate levels.

Polymeric plasticizers are frequently used in polyvinyl chloride compounding. Pearl resins are particularly recommended for applications in which appreciable quantities of these polymeric plasticizers are required. As shown in Table 6.3, the polymer will absorb up to 100 parts of "Paraplex" G-50, a commercial polymeric plasticizer. The flow rate of a dry blend made from this polymeric plasticizer and the Pearl resin is compared with the flow of a conventional resin-polymeric plasticizer blend in Figure 6.4. The Pearl polymer

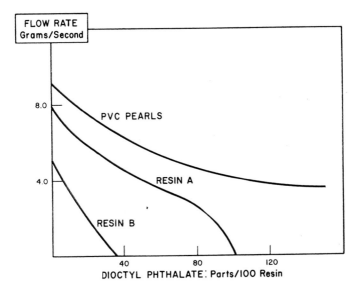

Figure 6.3. Flow of resin-plasticizer blends.

imparts excellent flow even when 80 parts of polymeric plasticizer is used. Dry blends made with conventional resins fail to flow at these high plasticizer levels.

TABLE 6.3. ABSORPTION OF POLYMERIC PLASTICIZER BY PVC RESINS

Resin	Parts "Paraplex" G-50 Per Hundred Resin	Dry Up Time Min.	Dry Blend Flow Rate g/sec.
PVC Pearls	—	—	9.1
PVC Pearls	30	1	10.0
PVC Pearls	50	5	10.0
PVC Pearls	70	40	10.0
PVC Pearls	100	60	Will not flow
A	—	—	7.7
A	30	1	7.7
A	50	6	7.7
A	70	60+	Will not flow

It is interesting to note that dry blends made with PVC Pearls and the polymeric plasticizer flow better at low plasticizer level than PVC Pearl-dioctyl phthalate blends. However, the total amount of dioctyl phthalate which can be absorbed is greater than the amount of "Paraplex" G-50 which the resin will absorb.

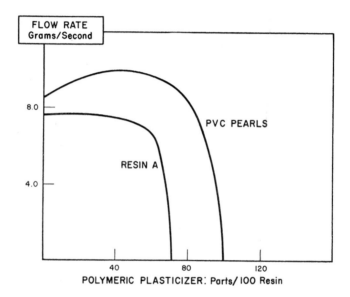

Figure 6.4. Flow of resin-plasticizer blends.

The flow rates of dry blends are outstanding. The large uniform particle size is probably responsible for these excellent flow properties, as there is no fine material to pack between the large particles. Also, the larger size presents a smaller surface for particle to particle contact and adhesion, thus yielding superior flow rates at all plasticizer levels, and making it possible to incorporate large amounts of plasticizer without fusing or caking.

Processing. PVC Pearl compounds may be extruded, milled or calendered in equipment normally used in the manufacture of plastic articles. The dry blends described above may be extruded directly and expensive milling or Banbury operation is eliminated. A number of extrusion studies of dry

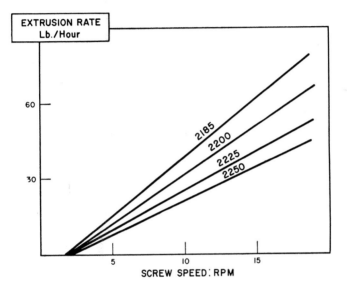

Figure 6.5. Extrusion of PVC pearls.

blends have been made. It was found that these dry blends extrude best under conditions which resemble those used for the extrusion of granulated compounds rather than conditions usually required for dry blends. Further, extrusion of Pearl compounds using the proper extruder conditions has resulted in a 25% increase in production over conventional dry blend resins in factory operations.

A study of the rate of extrusion as a function of the extruder screw speed was made. The extruder temperature and the compound used are shown in Table 6.4. The dry blends were extruded as strips from a 2½ in. National Rubber Machinery extruder having a L.D. ratio of 20/1. Four PVC Pearl resins were run: 2250, 2225, 2200 and 2185 representing high, medium low and very low molecular weight resin respectively. The results are shown in Figure 6.5. The extrusion rate versus screw speed data is best represented by a straight line for each of the resins studied. The resin having the highest molecular weight gave the lowest extrusion rate at a given screw speed. Thus, the fastest production rates are obtained with low molecular weight resins. The color and clarity of the extruded tapes from the PVC Pearl compounds were good and there was no evidence of imperfections.

TABLE 6.4. EXTRUSION OF PVC PEARLS

Pearl Resin	2250	2225	2200	2185
Relative viscosity 1% in cyclohexanone @25°C.	2.45	2.25	2.03	1.85
Specific viscosity ASTM D 1243-54	0.42	0.38	0.33	0.30
Extrusion Rates:				
Screw speed = 8 rpm	16	20	24	34
Screw speed = 11 rpm	24	27	38	46
Screw speed = 14 rpm	31	38	48	58
Screw speed = 16 rpm	39	44	52	68
Screw speed = 18 rpm	44	51	65	78

Extruder Temperatures		Compound	
Zone 1	260°F.	Pearl resin	100.0
Zone 2	320	Dioctyl phthalate	45.0
Zone 3	390	Epoxy plasticizer	5.0
Zone 4	410	Cadmium stabilizer	3.0
Gate	385	Stearic acid	0.5
Head	420		
Die	385		

The polymer was mixed in an internal mixer and calendered into film. This film was free of gelled particles or "fisheyes" and again exhibited unusually good color and clarity. It was heat-sealed with standard radio frequency heat-sealing equipment. The bonds were stronger than the film. The polymer can be extruded, milled or calendered in conventional plastics processing equipment.

Physical Properties. Pearl polymers of four different molecular weights were compounded with 42.5 parts of dioctyl phthalate and stabilized with a barium-cadmium-epoxy system. The physical properties of these compounds are shown in Table 6.5. As expected, the high molecular weight resin had the maximum tensile properties, abrasion resistance and heat resistance. These properties fell off as the molecular weight of the resin was reduced. In choosing a resin for a given use, one must remember that the best physical properties are obtained at high molecular weight, but that best processing is found when a low molecular weight resin is

TABLE 6.5. PHYSICAL PROPERTIES OF PVC PEARLS

Type	2250	2225	2200	2185
Relative viscosity 1% in cyclohexanone @ 25°C.	2.45	2.25	2.03	1.85
Specific viscosity ASTM D 1243-54	0.42	0.38	0.33	0.30
Tensile, psi	2900	2850	2650	2400
100% modulus, psi	2000	2000	1900	1850
Elongation, %	315	290	280	250
Hardness, Shore A	89	90	87	86
Tabor abrasion loss 2000 cycles, g	0.130	0.145	0.150	0.170
Heat resistance Min. to black @ 190°C.	90	75	60	45

Compound:

Resin	100.0
Dioctylphthalate	42.5
Barium-cadmium stabilizer	2.5
Epoxy stabilizer	1.0
Stearic acid	0.5

used. The user must select the resin which offers the best balance of physical properties and processing economics.

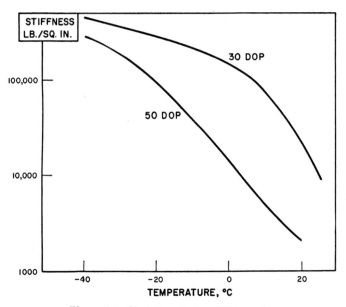

Figure 6.6. Clash-Berg test on PVC pearls.

The stiffness in torsion *vs.* temperature test developed by Clash and Berg (ASTM D 1043-51) was run on compounds prepared from these four PVC Pearl resins as shown in Figure 6.6. Each resin was run at two plasticizer levels, 30 and 50 parts of dioctyl phthalate. At each plasticizer level, a single curve represented the behavior of all four resins. Thus, while the plasticizer level has a significant effect, the molecular weight of the resin in the range reported here does not affect the low temperature properties of the compound.

Electrical Insulation Resistance. A large amount of polyvinyl chloride resin is used for the insulation of wire. Good electrical insulation properties, wide color range, ease of production and low cost are factors which make vinyls attractive.

The value of a polyvinyl chloride resin in electrical applications is best determined by preparing an electrical compound and actually insulating wire. The insulation resistance is measured while the wire is immersed in water. It is desirable to test over an extended period of time to account for such factors as aging, shrinkage, leaching and water absorption.

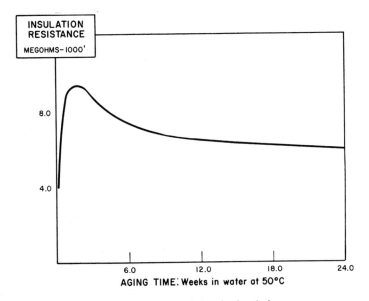

Figure 6.7. PVC pearls in wire insulation.

The high molecular weight polymer was compounded in an electrical stock as shown in Table 6.6, and this compound was extruded on #14 copper wire at about 300 ft per min. in a ⅟₃₂ in. insulation. The wire was immersed in water at 50°C., and the insulation resistance was measured over a period of 24 weeks. The results of this test are shown in Figure 6.7. The insulation resistance of the Pearl compound is quite constant during the testing period, indicating that the compound has good aging qualities. The equilibrium insulation resistance of 6.5 megohms-1,000 feet is well above the Underwriters' requirements of 0.1 megohms-1,000 feet.

TABLE 6.6. PVC ELECTRICAL INSULATION COMPOUND

PVC Pearls	100.0
DOP (electrical grade)	52.0
Basic lead carbonate	10.0
Clay (Pigment 33)	7.0
Lead stearate	0.5

The resin was evaluated by a large insulated wire manufacturer. Aging studies showed that the insulation compound retained 94% of its original elongation after aging seven days at 113°C., while the retention of elongation of a good electrical grade commercial PVC resin was only 88% in the same test.

The good insulating properties of compounds based on the Pearl polymer, together with the ease of extrusion directly from dry blends, suggest that this resin is ideal for some electrical applications.

Rigids. The Pearl polymers are particularly well suited for rigid applications. A low molecular weight polymer is usually preferred, as plasticizers are excluded or used at very low levels and optimum processing properties are required. The low molecular weight polymer (type 2200) was stabilized with 3% of dibutyl tin mercaptide and milled on a 16-in. differential speed mill at 177°C. stock temperature. The compound was found to band quickly and a smooth, rolling bank was obtained. The heat stability of the compound was outstanding compared to commercial polymers as shown in Table 6.7. The physical properties were determined and all the resins studied were found to be equivalent.

The low molecular weight PVC Pearl resins are recommended for rigid applications in which normal heat distortion and impact strength, low temperature processing, good color, clarity and heat resistance are required.

TABLE 6.7. PROPERTIES OF PVC RIGID COMPOUNDS

	PVC Pearls Type 2200	Resin C	Resin D
Relative viscosity			
1% in cyclohexanone @ 25°C.	2.10	2.14	1.84
Milled @ 177°C.			
Time to discolor minutes	90	40	30
Heat distortion temperature, °C.			
Fiber stress at 66 psi	80	80	—
Heat distortion temperature, °C.			
Fiber stress of 264 psi	75	75	74
Izod impact, ft lb/inch of notch	0.82	0.88	0.70

Compound:	
Resin	100.0
Dibutyl tin mercaptide	3.0

Superpolyoxymethylene ("Delrin")

A new thermoplastic has been created by duPont. This resin, registered as "Delrin," is an acetal with the structure of polyoxymethylene. The high-melting, highly crystalline polymer is a real achievement in the polymer world. This new plastic is not a vinyl, and the data here given are solely for the purpose of presenting this outstanding new polymer development. DuPont is currently constructing a plant near Parkersburg, West Virginia, and it is expected that the polymer will be commercially available in mid-1959.

A paper describing the properties, fabrication and end-use testing was presented by Cogdell and Hardesty of duPont at the 14th Annual National Technical Conference of the SPE in 1958. Early tests show "Delrin" has an excellent combination of high strength, flexual modulus, fatigue life,

Vinyl Resins

resilience and toughness. Much of the early test work has been done on limited quantities of polymer and the data here presented are preliminary. Two types of resin have been studied and are described as "Delrin" 500X for general purpose molding and "Delrin" 150-X for general-purpose extrusion.

Formaldehyde is a molecule of exceptional reactivity. The polymerization of formaldehyde in water with an ionic catalyst to form a low molecular weight solid has been known for a long time. The resulting low polymer has poor mechanical properties and low thermal stability. DuPont has prepared a stable superpolyoxymethylene which normally averages more than 1,000 CH_2O units. Thus the polymer is a linear acetal resin. High molecular weight polyoxymethylene is prepared utilizing catalysts which are quaternary ammonium salt, quaternary phosphonium salt, or a tertiary sulfonium salt as a polymerization initiator. Inherent viscosities of the polymer were measured at 150°C., utilizing solutions of 0.5 g of polymer in 100 ml of dimethyformamide containing 1 g of diphenylamine.

An example of the polymer preparation is the pyrolysis of cyclohexyl hemiformal, and then the fractional condensing of the pyrolysis vapors to effect a separation of formaldehyde vapor from cyclohexanol and water condensate. The formaldehyde vapors are passed in series through two cold traps packed with glass helices and maintained at 0°C. Formaldehyde vapors leaving the cold traps are introduced into a continuous 2-liter reactor containing toluene at 0°C. as the reaction medium. The polymerization initiator in this case is an equimolar mixture of tetra-*n*-butylammonium iodide and lauric acid dissolved in toluene. All ingredients are pumped continuously into the reactor, and a polymeric dispersion product is continuously removed at such a rate that the contact time is about ten minutes. The reaction medium is pumped into the reactor at such a rate that the average holdup volume in the reactor is 600 ml. Formaldehyde vapors are passed into the reactor at a rate of about 8 g per min.

The initiator solution is injected into the reaction medium so that the concentration of the quaternary ammonium iodide is 1.87 mg per liter of reaction medium and the concentration of lauric acid is 0.99 mg per liter of reaction medium. The contents of the reactor are agitated at 65°C., and the polymeric product is produced at a rate of 396 grams per liter of reaction medium per hour. After filtering, washing, and drying, the snow-white polymeric formaldehyde product is found to exhibit an inherent viscosity of 0.67. The maximum inherent viscosity reported in a South African patent application is 1.65.

It may be significant that the patent application for this process states that the high molecular weight polyoxymethylene may be further treated with acetic anhydride to esterify any substituent hydroxyl groups and thereafter be fabricated into high quality films, fibers, filaments, and molded articles. The lowest film brittleness temperature reported of this esterified polymer was —95°C.

MacDonald of duPont in U. S. Patent 2,768,994 suggests that superpolyoxymethylene possibly differs from its low molecular precursors because the method of introducing the monomer into the reaction medium results in polymerization as fast as the monomer contacts the reaction medium. This may effect some purification of the monomer, of the reaction medium, or of both. He further speculates that there may also be such a small amount of formaldehyde monomer present at any one time that the many well known reactions of formaldehyde do not take place to any appreciable extent, with the result that the superpolymer process produces longer and stronger chains of recurring (CH_2O) units with less foreign, and possibly weak, elements in the chain. This patent states agitation is conducted in a mixture of decahydronaphthalene containing a nonionic dispersing agent made by completely esterifying a polyethylene glycol of molecular weight of 400 with oleic acid.

"Delrin's" fatigue endurance limit of 5,000 psi at 72°F. and 100% relative humidity is a higher limit than that obtained with any other typical thermoplastics under similar conditions. This superiority of the superpolyoxymethylene becomes more apparent as the temperature is increased. Notched Izod impact strengths of 1.4 and 1.7 ft-lb/in. are slightly higher than Type I PVC. Little loss of impact strength is suffered by "Delrin," even at temperatures as low as −40°. The polymer has very good abrasion resistance and in general is superior to other commercially available thermoplastics, with the exception of nylon.

There is no variation in the coefficient of friction of "Delrin" over a temperature range of 73° to 250°F. and under loads of up to 2500 psi. The polymer is one of the few materials which combines excellent electrical properties with exceptional mechanical characteristics. The dielectric strength (short time) is 500 volts/mil and the volume resistivity 6×10^{14} ohm/cm (0.2% water) and the surface resistivity 2×10^{13} ohm. As a result of low moisture absorption (0.9% maximum) the polymer has good electrical resistance after exposure at high humidities and complete water immersion.

The chemical resistance is most unusual as there are no common solvents for "Delrin" at low temperatures. The material is not recommended for use in contact with strong acids or strong bases. Permeability when exposed to aliphatic and aromatic hydrocarbons, halogenated hydrocarbons, alcohols and esters is only a fraction of that of polyethylene. This may make packaging applications possible. However, permeability to water vapor is significantly greater than that of polyethylene. The polymer is attacked by ultraviolet light, but has excellent service life in air and water.

The opaque white polymer can be colored by a variety of

compositions. The burning rate is comparable to polyethylene and polystyrene. No toxic problems are presented when the polymer is used for dishware and common household utensils.

Test items were machined from rods and plaques, extruded from new and existing dies and molded.

DuPont has tested more than 100 applications using "Delrin" in mechanical, automotive, plumbing and hardware, appliances, packaging and many consumer items. Mechanical applications are for gears, valves, wedges, caps and knobs. Consumer items are tableware, knife handles, pen barrels, combs and pipe stems. Packaging items include aerosol bottles, sprayer nozzles, etc. Blow molding of aerosol containers is believed to offer good sale prospect as the containers have good tensile strength, stiffness, toughness, low creep, chemical resistance, low permeability, high gloss and a wide range of color possibilities. Good dimensional stability in the presence of water led to successful tests as plumbing fixtures in showerheads. Fabrication of the polymer into bearings, gears, and bushings appear equally promising.

The economy of injection molding indicates that "Delrin" will be technically satisfactory and cost less than some machined steel gears. "Delrin" has been molded in machines ranging in size from 1 to 60 oz. A variety of molds—single cavity, temporary, die casting, cam-action and multi-cavity up to 100 cavities—have given good performance. Extruders ranging in size from 1 to 4½ inches have been successful in producing sheet, pipe, rod, tubing and blow molded bottles. "Delrin" 500X is in a molding range comparable in melt viscosity to "Alathon" 14 polyethylene. Molding can be performed at any temperature between 160 and 250°F., and it is suggested that optimum surface gloss can be obtained by molding at the higher temperature.

DuPont points out that "Delrin" 150X is a high viscosity material specifically designed for extrusion, with a melt viscosity in the same range as "Lucite" 140 acrylic resin and

"Zytel" 42 nylon resin. Extrusions are recommended using long barrels with ratios of length to diameter of 20:1. Either electrical heating or oil heating may be used on the barrels. The barrel heaters are generally set for 390-400°F., along the entire length. These conditions give stock temperatures of approximately 390°F.

A general statement of the outstanding properties of "Delrin" is that its solvent resistance is better than that of any other thermoplastic except the fluorocarbons. The resin has abrasion resistance exceeded by nylon only, approaches aluminum in strength, is dimensionally stable, expanding only 40% when immersed in water (less than nylon), and possesses excellent deformation recovery. In fact, "Delrin" is expected to complement nylon in properties and applications, and may be used in some applications now using nylon where nylon's higher melting point is not required. Present day "Delrin" does not readily accept adhesives and inks. The price of the polymer is expected to be in the same range as nylon.

Rigid PVC Film

Calenders are available from Berstorff in Hanover, Germany, which cost about $350,000 installed and have a maximum capacity of one million pounds per year of film slightly over 3 ft wide and 1 mil thick. West German production of rigid PVC film in 1957 is estimated to be about 3,000 tons, ranging from 1.2 to 8 mils in thickness. Material has been calendered as thin as 0.4 mil. Extrusion and blowing techniques are not used in Germany. The thinner gauged film is stretched either unilaterally or bilaterally. The maximum unilateral stretching is 3.5 times the original length. German practice finds it not practical to calender to less than 1.5 mils before stretching.

Calendered rigid PVC film was originally made from a specially washed emulsion polymer with a K-value of 75-85.

There are now several grades of emulsion vinyl which can be used as well as suspension polymer. The Germans state that it is essential in the manufacture of rigid film to use polymer of uniform quality in order to avoid processing difficulties. There are indications that in some cases emulsion and suspension polymers are used in combination. Anorgana is using suspension polymer in combination with an undisclosed and odorless nontoxic stabilizer which may be a mixture of diphenyl thiourea and a wax. Their "Genotherm" film is clear and of excellent quality, and has been approved for use in food packaging (see Chapter 5).

The largest four roll calender made by Berstorff for rigid PVC film has rolls 550 mm in diameter and 1200 mm wide with a working speed range from 2 to 20 meters per minute. This type of calender was recently purchased from Berstorff by Minnesota Mining. The largest use of thin rigid PVC film in West Germany is for packaging followed by sound recording and pressure-sensitive tape. The material is laminated to paper or aluminum foil or used in the unsupported form. Major packaging application is for oleomargarine and other fatty materials where polyethylene would not be suitable. Film for lamination and vacuum forming is usually not stretched, while sound recording and pressure-sensitive tapes are stretched unilaterally and unsupported package film stretched bilaterally. A big new development is the packaging of oleomargarine in a container which consists of rigid PVC film laminated between two layers of wax paper. Vacuum forming of unplasticized film in Germany is promising.

Polyvinyl Alcohol Film

PVA film is briefly described in Chapter 5. It is a relative newcomer to the plastics world and has enjoyed some degree of success. A number of applications have been suggested including packaging for various soap powders and detergents, insecticides, dyes, dangerous chemicals and disinfectants. The water-soluble containers and the entire package are added to the water without breaking the package or removing the wrapper. When used in the preparation of these packages, the package added directly to water dissolves in seconds, exposing the contents for solubility. A certain degree of time saving and material losses are so provided. Good film flexibility and extensibility permit use as a mold-release agent in the preparation of polyesters, epoxies, phenolics, and rubber in pressure and vacuum bag molding applications. The film is stated to be suitable for packaging fatty foods such as butter. Radioactive studies have established that polyvinyl alcohol is not extracted by edible fats and oils, and thus suggesting it can be safely used for wrapping fatty foods. It has been used as a camelback to prevent sticking of rubber sheeting. When applied in solution rubber rolls are protected from abrasion and solvent attack. The transparency, tear-resistance, and high strength suggest its use in various coverings such as aprons and garment covers. PVA film is not recommended for moisture proofness or where high water resistance is required.

The film is generally soluble in hot water, but insolubility can be imparted by the addition of an aldehyde (furfural) and an acid catalyst. A somewhat more practical approach is to use a water-soluble formaldehyde derivative such as dimethylol urea. This method requires the addition of dimethylol urea and a catalyst to the PVA solution, and after its application the insolubilizing reaction is completed by heating at 100-110°C. In addition to the above described method, increased water resistance is imparted by chromium compounds. Cupric dichromate in concentrations of 2-5% based on the polymer is dissolved in water and added to the PVA solution shortly before using and the composition heated to 100°C. The film has an unusually high degree of gas impermeability to oxygen, hydrogen, nitrogen, carbon dioxide and "Freon." Exceptions are water vapor and ammonia. An average tensile strength is approximately 10,000 psi before stretching and about 50,000 psi after stretching to five times the original length. Shore Durometer hardness over 100 is found in unplasticized material.

Film can be cast from solution of partially hydrolyzed polymer with solids contents of 60-65%. If maximum strength is required higher molecular weight polymer must be used, perhaps incorporated with 10-20% of a plasticizer. Oriented film is light-polarizing and can be used for manufacture of sun glasses and certain photographic applications. Solutions containing a dichromate cast into film form are made insoluble by exposure to ultraviolet light. This property is useful in the preparation of stencil screens and lithographic paper printing plates. In such an application the printing surface is obtained by exposing this particular film to ultraviolet light through a design and then washing away the soluble portion with water.

Monomer MG-1

Carbide and Carbon was issued U. S. patent 2,618,621 in November, 1952. This patent pertains to use of polyglycol methacrylates as a plasticizer in conjunction with DOP. The function of the material is actually one of a "non-plasticizing plasticizer." The material is marketed by Carbide as "Monomer MG-1" and is described as a polyethylene glycol dimethacrylate. The patent speaks of polyethylene glycol which is esterified with methacrylic acid in which the glycol involved may have average molecular weights of 106 (monomer), 200, 300, and 400.

The high-boiling, low viscosity product is principally used in the manufacture of rigid or semi-rigid materials from vinyl plastisols. In this function MG-1 acts as a dispersant for the resin and replaces part of a conventional plasticizer. In the fusion cycle it polymerizes under the influence of a catalyst to produce a rigid resin. It can also be used to cross-link other resins by vinyl addition. The polymerization is mildly exo-thermic, and it is essential that a free radical type catalyst be used to assure adequate rate of polymerization. Some of the catalysts which have been employed are benzoyl peroxide, *t*-butyl perbenzoate, di-tertiary butyl peroxide, and methyl ethyl ketone peroxide. Hydroquinone present as an inhibitor need not be removed before use of the monomer. The value of MG-1 is that after polymerization the material no longer functions as a plasticizer but imparts rigidity.

The plastisols which contain the polyglycol dimethacrylates may be prepared by stirring emulsion PVC or copolymer in the plasticizer mixture or by grinding the resins and plasti-cizers in a three-roll mill. The peroxide catalyst concentra-tion as disclosed in the patent is from 0.5 to 5%. Incorpora-tion of a polymerization inhibitor (hydroquinone) may be needed to inhibit premature polymerization. The polymeriza-tion temperatures are normally 325-375°F., as above 400°F. some degradation occurs. Incipient polymerization with ben-zoyl peroxide is at 250°F. Tin mercaptide stabilizers are polymerization inhibitors as are dissolved air, carbon black, and some phosphite chelators. Metal naphthenates and iron and lead salts are accelerators. Cured plastisol obtains its maximum stiffness after heating for two or three minutes at 320°F. It is stated that in order to obtain suspensions of proper fluidity, it is essential to utilize finely divided resin. The amount of MG-1 required varies but the formulation may contain 10-30 PHR plus sufficient DOP to produce the desired flexibility. The total charge of the dimethacrylate and conventional plasticizer may be 60 parts.

Recommended uses are in rigid or semi-rigid toys, wire coatings, sprayable plastisols, rigid and semi-rigid rotational castings and in vinyl foams. Clear film has been made by Carbide using 100 parts of dispersion resin, 60 parts MG-1 and 1.8 parts *t*-butyl perbenzoate as a catalyst, and curing the plastisol one minute at 375°F. Half of the monomer may be replaced by DOP which prolongs the cure time to as long as 5 min. The semi-rigid films are more highly colored than film cast on aluminum foil from plastisol resin using DOP alone.

It is believed that the use and development of MG-1 has not progressed as rapidly as some predictions made for it. The cost of the monomer ($1.00 l.c.l) is high, and the curing is difficult to control. This writer cannot appraise the potential of monomer MG-1 at this date.

Vinyl Esters

Vinyl butyrate is the most important of the vinyl esters for polymerization. Other esters are now commercially available although sale of most is limited. These include vinyl formate, propionate, 2-ethylhexoate, crotonate, levulinate, and stearate (see Chapter 3 for discussion of vinyl stearate polymer). These monomers are polymerized or copolymerized by the general methods previously described. Literature references to copolymerization with these vinyl esters include vinyl acetate, vinyl chloride and acrylonitrile. In addition, successful copolymerizations have been effected with acrylic acid and its esters, methacrylic esters, butadiene and styrene, maleic anhydride and its esters and acrylamide.

Polyvinyl propionate prepared by emulsion polymerization produces a material of better water resistance, adhesion, and flexibility than polyvinyl acetate. Polymers and copolymers are being studied for possible applications as safety glass adhesives, coatings, laminating resins, water-based paints, films, textile and leather finishes, adhesives, and chewing gum resins. Tensile strength of films in some cases is decidedly higher than films of vinyl chloride-vinyl acetate. The old problem of internal plasticization has prompted many copolymerizations in an attempt to obtain inherent flexibility. This search goes on as a good solution to this problem is not yet available. Polyvinyl formate is quite resistant to gasoline and due to such may have special application. Vinyl crotonate can be used to cross-link some other resinous materials.

Medical Applications of Vinyl Tubing

The field of medicinal applications utilizing principally vinyl tubing has now grown to be big business. Some vinyl film, also non-toxic, is used. PVC tubing utilizing non-toxic plasticizers and stabilizers is widely used for intravenous injections of anesthetics, glucose and saline solutions, and plasma. A heart catheter is made of thin tubing which is inserted into a vein in the arm and threaded until it enters the heart cavities. PVC is applicable due to its flexibility, non-toxic nature, excellent sound conductivity and sterilizability. U. S. Stoneware is a leader in preparation of medical tubing. It is quite conceivable that tubing of this nature will be used in even greater volume by the beverage and dairy industries.

Polyvinylpyrrolidone

The early work of Reppe in Germany on high pressure reactions of acetylene in the decade preceding World War II has been continued by General Aniline & Film in this country. Large quantities of polyvinylpyrrolidone have been stocked here and abroad for military and civilian use for formulation into blood plasma volume expander solutions. This material was accumulated in the belief the PVP may be a superior shock solution when supplies of whole blood and plasma are unavailable. A possible use of PVP in normal saline for this application is as a 3.5% solution of an approximate average molecular weight of 40,000. PVP also is used to detoxify iodine without impairing germicidal and virucidal properties.

PVP is not a "new" polymer, but many of its applications are entirely new and it is conceivable that sale of the product will accelerate. The use of the monomer (or polymer) in conjunction with certain synthetic fibers such as the acrylics, markedly improves dye acceptance. General Aniline & Film has performed excellent research and development on vinyl-pyrrolidone and its polymers. The product is supplied in three forms specified as K-30, K-60 and K-90. K-30 is a white, free-flowing powder of 95% active ingredient, while K-60 and K-90 are aqueous solutions of 45 and 20%, respectively.

Relatively small amounts of the polymer are effective stabilizers for emulsions, suspensions, and dispersions. The material cross-links with a number of materials including polyacrylic acid to form insoluble complexes in water and alcohol. In addition to iodine PVP binds various toxins, viruses, dyes, potent drugs and other chemicals thereby reducing toxicity and irritation.

Use of this polymer as a drug retardant is quite marked when administered in conjunction with procaine, the combination producing longer anesthesia in the circulation and tissues. With antibiotics the potency and duration of the drug is enhanced. Aerosol hair sprays are now well accepted, and preparations containing 2-5% PVP are marketed. PVP is also incorporated in hair tints, shampoos, shaving products, skin creams, lipsticks, sun tan products, deodorants, and dentifrices. Good bonding occurs on smooth surfaces such as glass, metals and plastics when used as an additive with solution or emulsion type adhesives. Incorporation in detergent formulations gives superior suspending action on soil in both cellulose and synthetic fibers. Dyeability of acrylic fibers is improved by incorporation into the coagulated and still swollen spun product before or after partial orientation. The fiber utilizing 5-10% PVP is receptive to many dyes (see Table 2.10). Stripping operations of paper are effective in removing dye from rag stock by use of 2% PVP on the fiber weight. Protective coatings incorporate the polymer as a dispersant and protective colloid for paints. Use in waxes and polishes functions as a protective colloid and film former. PVP clarifies and chillproofs beverages for beer, whisky, wine and fruit juice production. One of the newest suggested uses is in the preparation of wettable formulations for spraying, dusting and seeding of crops. It is not known whether all of these applications are commercial.

Radiation

Radioisotopes are still confined mainly to applications non-chemical in nature. Radiation absorption is used for measurement of thickness of film. The increased yield of radioactive fission products will eventually make radioactive polymerization more practical and less expensive. The various vinyl monomers which are polymerized by addition type mechanisms are dependent upon free radicals and therefore can be initiated by radionuclides. It is believed that work to date on polymerization of vinyl chloride has been confined to experimental studies by all except St. Gobain. St. Gobain at one time was believed to be commercially producing PVC using cobalt 60 as an initiator, but this is thought to be commercially abandoned. Graft polymers initiated by radionuclides produce marked changes in the polymers. Graft polymerization of PVC and various monomers has been experimentally studied, and it has been found that PVC and acrylonitrile so polymerized have higher thermal resistance. This may result in producing polymers of PVC which may be entirely adequate for piping of hot water. Attendant with increased resistance to thermal degradation is a marked decrease in tensile strength in many polymerizations and also the production of unsaturation which makes the polymer susceptible to oxidative attack.

It is quite possible that the appreciable cost of initiation by radioactive means will be greatly reduced in the future, and this cost of up to 5-cents per pound of polymer may be so decreased as to make this means of polymerization economically feasible.

New Equipment

References have been made in the text to certain articles of equipment which have only recently become commercial. Perhaps the most significant for fabrication of vinyls has been the new high-speed calenders. Among the more prominent are those of Adamson United Company and Farrell-Birmingham Company, which can reputedly produce 12,000 yd of sheeting per hour (see Chapter 4). Many sizes and types of calenders are made which vary from the small 8 x 16-in. rolls up to and including 36 x 92-in. These companies manufacture 2-roll, 3-roll vertical, 3-roll 120°, 4-roll inverted-L, and Z calenders. Adamson has a patented roll bending device. Some calenders also provide roll crossing devices which are a means of controlling gauge of the calendered film or sheeting. Roll bending permits precise control of thickness of calendered film and sheeting by applying a bending moment to off-set the bending of the calender rolls caused by pressure generated in squeezing the formulation. Farrell-Birmingham has improved the design of 4-roll Z calenders by positioning the lower assembly at an angle. This facilitates access to all rolls, is advantageous for threading and operating, and permits closer installation of auxiliary equipment. Individual drives for each of the 4 rolls can be provided.

The trend in the design of calenders is toward higher roll temperatures, greater roll-separating forces, and a wider range of available friction ratios. Most plastics calenders have two-speed, motorized roll adjustment with the low speed designed for use with automatic gauging. Beta-ray gauging equipment as presently designed controls the longitudinal and edge gauge as well as the center gauge through crossed-axes motor control.

FUTURE OF THE VINYLS

Indications of the growth prospects of each of the vinyl plastics presented herein is described in other chapters. It may be well to bring into focus some of these more apparent trends which this industry may face in 1965-1975. The "workhorse" of the vinyls, vinyl chloride and its copolymers, is adequately presented in Tables 1.1 and 1.2. Quick examination of these tables indicates fields of very rapid growth. These are molding and extrusion and flooring. Wire extrusion and various profiles continue to show accelerated potential. It would not be surprising to find the flooring industry consuming three to five times their present consumption of the vinyls by 1975. New applications for film and sheeting such as the agricultural uses described may well make this now relatively stable sale one of enormous growth. These applications for film and sheeting seem more speculative at this writing than molding, extrusion, and flooring applications. The 11-cent reduction in price of PVC between 1952 and 1956 will increase the sale outlook for this most versatile of plastics.

Two supposedly "sleeping giants" are vinyl foam and rigids. Both of these fields offer vast potential, and yet a strong element of uncertainty accompanies them. This author if forced to make a prediction believes that consumption of vinyls in rigid applications by 1965 and later will far outstrip resin utilized in vinyl foams.

Dispersion resins indicate decided tendencies for major growth in slush and rotational molding applications.

Vinyls other than vinyl chloride and its copolymers which have brightest industrial possibilities probably rest with polyvinyl acetate. Vinyl paints have come from a most insignificant position to that of a serious challenger to the entire water-based latex paint field. Vinyl acetate adhesives were a 30 million pound item in 1957. The total consumption of polyvinyl

acetate both homopolymer and copolymer in 1957 is estimated to be approximately 75 million pounds. It seems
plausible that this important member of the vinyl family will
at least double in volume by 1975.

(Courtesy Jet Propulsion Laboratory)

Figure 6.8. The Corporal surface-to-surface guided missile protected
against weather by vinyl "raincoat."

The emphasis on missiles and defense preparation has not ignored the vinyls. It is not foreseeable what direction vinyls will play in this future of military and other applications, but it is certainly logical that many uses presently undreamed of will appear in profusion. The building industry continues to boom and uses for many types of plastics are increasing. The agricultural industry remains a big question mark, but here again certain specialty applications in this vast sale picture can change the film and sheeting stability to one of major increase. Vinyls in packaging are as yet relatively small in scope. The unique properties of the resins may someday make the packaging field a major source of outlet. The development of non-toxic formulations, both rigid and flexible, could initiate volume sale in the packaging field. Vinylidene chloride copolymer would appear to have its relatively modest sale growth prospect largely in the preparation of film and coating resins.

It is problematical to state that the vinyl resins output by 1960 will be one billion pounds. However, it would certainly seem reasonably safe in our present economy to state that 1965 will surely result in a total sale of at least one billion pounds of all of the vinyl resins.

INDEX